Higher
ENGLISH

The Scottish Certificate of Education Examination Papers
are reprinted by special permission of
THE SCOTTISH QUALIFICATIONS AUTHORITY

ISBN 0 7169 9280 9
© *Robert Gibson & Sons, Glasgow, Ltd., 1998*

ROBERT GIBSON · Publisher
17 Fitzroy Place, Glasgow, G3 7SF.

SCOTTISH
CERTIFICATE OF
EDUCATION
1994

FRIDAY, 6 MAY
9.15 AM – 11.20 AM

ENGLISH
HIGHER GRADE
Paper I

There are TWO PARTS to this paper, Part 1 (Interpretation) and Part 2 (Report). Both should be attempted.

NB In Part 1 (Interpretation) there are two passages, and questions.

Use the left-hand margin of the answer book to indicate clearly the questions attempted.

Your answer to Part 2 (Report) should begin on a fresh page.

Part 1 is worth 40 marks.

Part 2 is worth 35 marks.

PART 1—INTERPRETATION

Attempt all of Part 1. You should spend approximately 1 hour on this part of the paper, including reading time. There are TWO passages and questions.

Read both passages carefully and then answer all the questions which follow **on page four. Use your own words whenever possible**. The number of marks attached to each question will give a clear indication of the length of answer required.

It is important that you read both passages before you attempt to answer any of the questions.

The subject of both passages is the River Thames. Passage 1 is taken from an essay by Jonathan Raban in which the writer explores what the river means to London and its people. In Passage 2 the river provides the setting for an incident in Charles Dickens's novel, Our Mutual Friend.

PASSAGE 1

ON THE WATER MARGIN

It's wrong to say, as people almost always do, that London does not use its river. The Thames has never been the city's chief point of focus like the Seine in Paris or the Grand Canal in Venice. Yet
5 London, no less than Venice or Paris, uses its river to define itself. The Thames marks the edge of things. It is what makes north London north, and south London south. Like a twisty ruler, it measures out the intricate social and economic
10 gradations between the east and west of the city. But the Thames is a boundary, not a thoroughfare, and like all boundaries it is there for people to turn back from. So London characteristically faces away from its river. It lives, even now, in a mental
15 world where The Strand really is a strand—a border, edge, or coast. Modern attempts to break with this convention, like the South Bank complex, have an odd feel to them: Londoners have been using their river for so long as a looping no-man's-
20 land that it is difficult to adjust to a perspective which faces across the river rather than turning away from it.

It is not so much from neglect as from proper respect that the river is treated like this. More than
25 any other city river, the Thames is associated with the mysterious margins of society. In Dickens it is laden with corpses, as black and foreboding as the Styx*. Nor was it any accident that the notorious Vauxhall Pleasure Gardens of the 18th century
30 were ranged on the far bank of the river, on the other side of no-man's-land. Boundaries are places where laws and social rules become uncertain, where licence thrives and anything can happen. They are also places to which people who feel
35 themselves to be marginal, out on the far edge of society, naturally graduate.

In eight years of living in London, I've found myself tending again and again to the river for consolation. When things won't go, when
40 depression, like a giant squid, gets one in its grip,

the Thames is there to clear one's head, to mooch and mutter by. It is the one part of London where gravity, sadness, a sense of loss always seem in place.

Below Westminster, the river belongs to
45 melodrama. At Dockside, just beneath Tower Bridge on the south bank, one can wander among empty warehouses that still smell of cinnamon, where tramp fires smoulder on the upper floors and Tooley Streeters sleep out the day on acrid sacks. It
50 used to be called Saint Saviour's Dock, and was rechristened "Savoury Dock" because of the stench of "Folly Ditch", the open sewer that flowed into it. This was where the cholera epidemic of 1849 started—in the tiny houses that leaned together
55 over the neck of the dock; and it was here that Dickens set the scene of Bill Sikes's death in *Oliver Twist*. It is still a shadowy, forbidding place; it's hard to look into the inert, scummy water of the dock inlet without expecting to see a body there.

60 Or there is the extraordinary wide sweep of the river past the Isle of Dogs. The Isle itself is one of the most desolate places I have ever seen: its docks deserted, windows smashed, walls spray-gunned. The Dogs now are lacklustre Alsatians with bad
65 teeth, snarling in yards from behind chickenwire fences, guarding rusted heaps of chains, old cars and broken window-frames. The tower blocks are examples of the civic mind at its most brutish; the featureless green-space is a windy waste where only
70 the dogs dare to venture. Yet this violent, uncared-for, desecrated place looks out on the longest, widest and most beautiful of all the reaches of the Thames. Nowhere is the idea of the river as a boundary more marked than here. The Isle of
75 Dogs, with its heroic decrepitude, faces the stately, long, low wedding cake of Greenwich. One might be on the frontier between Korea and Switzerland.

(Jonathan Raban)

---

* *Styx: in Greek mythology, the underground river across which the dead were ferried to the Underworld.*

PASSAGE 2

As they glided slowly on, keeping under the shore, and sneaking in and out among the shipping, by back-alleys of water, in a pilfering way that seemed to be their boatman's normal manner of
5 progression, all the objects among which they crept were so huge in contrast with their wretched boat as to threaten to crush it. Not a ship's hull, with its rusty iron links of cable run out of hawse-holes long discoloured with the iron's rusty tears, but seemed
10 to be there with a grim intention. Not a figure-head but had the menacing look of bursting forward to run them down. Not a sluice-gate, or a painted scale upon a post or wall, showing the depth of water, but seemed to hint, like the dreadfully facetious Wolf in
15 bed in Grandmamma's cottage, "That's to drown you in, my dears!" Not a lumbering black barge, with its cracked and blistered side impending over them, but seemed to suck at the river with a thirst for sucking them under. And everything so vaunted
20 the spoiling influences of water—discoloured copper, rotten wood, honey-combed stone, green dank deposit—that the after-consequences of being crushed, sucked under, and drawn down, looked as ugly to the imagination as the main event.

25 Some half-hour of this work, and Riderhood unshipped his sculls, stood holding on to a barge, and hand over hand longwise along the barge's side gradually worked his boat under her head into a secret little nook of scummy water. And driven into
30 that nook, and wedged as he had described, was Gaffer's boat; that boat with the stain still in it, bearing some resemblance to a muffled human form.

"Now tell me I'm a liar!" said the honest Riderhood.

(*Charles Dickens*)

QUESTIONS FOR PART 1—INTERPRETATION

Questions on Passage 1

Marks

(a) Read the first two sentences of the passage, and explain briefly how the Thames is used differently from the Seine and the Grand Canal.　　1

(b) "The Thames marks the edge of things." (lines 6–7)

By referring to any single words or brief phrases from lines 7–16, explain how the writer develops this idea.　　3

(c) "It is not so much . . . is treated like this." (lines 23–24)

Show how this sentence acts as an important link between the first and second paragraphs.　　2

(d) A sinister aspect of the Thames emerges from the second paragraph.

Choose **two** phrases from lines 24–36 and, by close examination of the language used, show how each phrase helps to create this sinister aspect.　　4

(e) Give the meaning of "licence" as it is used in line 33, and explain briefly how the context has helped you to arrive at the meaning.　　2

(f) Read again the whole of the third paragraph (lines 37–43).

Using your own words, describe clearly **two** types of circumstance in which the writer finds himself "tending again and again to the river".　　2

(g) The language of lines 45–52 centres on the sense of smell.

By close reference to **three** separate words from these lines, show how effective each word is in contributing to the atmosphere of the scene as a whole.　　3

(h) It is said that the Isle of Dogs has been so-called since the fourteenth century, when King Edward III kennelled his favourite hunting hounds there.

By close reference to **two** examples from the text of lines 61–70 ("The Isle itself ... dare to venture."), show that the Isle has changed for the worse since the time of Edward III.　　2

(i) Show how the word "Yet" in line 70 marks an important turning-point in the writer's line of thought.　　2

(j) Read again from "Nowhere is the idea . . ." (line 73) to the end of the passage.

Explain, with close reference to the writer's word-choice, to what extent you find the lines fitting as a conclusion to the passage as a whole.　　3

(24)

Questions on Passage 2

(k) Explain how the structure of the opening sentence of this passage reflects the idea of the phrase "in a pilfering way" (line 3).　　2

(l) From lines 7–19, choose **two** examples of familiar objects and explain how each of these objects comes to take on sinister connotations. (You might consider such features as word-choice, sentence-structure, imagery, and so on.)　　4

(m) Explain briefly the purpose of the dashes in lines 20 and 22.　　1

(n) Explain how the final line helps you to deduce the reason for the journey described in this passage.　　2

(9)

Questions on Both Passages

(o) By referring closely to specific examples from both passages, comment on the extent to which you find that the passages contain significant similarities in descriptive language.　　4

(p) For Jonathan Raban, the river Thames is a boundary; for Dickens it is a thoroughfare.

From your reading of both passages, provide in your own words evidence to support the truth of these assertions.　　3

(7)

Total marks (40)

You should spend approximately one hour on this part of the paper, which is worth 35 marks.

READ THE INSTRUCTIONS BEFORE YOU ATTEMPT THIS QUESTION

(i) *Newspaper Articles*

IT HAS BECOME FASHIONABLE TO SLEEP ROUGH ON THE STREETS

Scottish MP Bill Walker has just spent two nights sleeping rough in Cardboard City.

On a miserable, wet night under a large bush in London's Lincoln Inn Fields earlier this month, the Tayside MP Bill Walker could be found inside two cardboard boxes and a Salvation Army-issue blanket.

Between 2,000 and 3,000 sleep rough in London every night, where almost every sheltered spot along The Strand and The Embankment has become home to beggars, drunks, the mentally ill and the rejected.

"I went out believing that many people were in that position through choice—either their choice or that of their family," he says. "That hardly changed at all; only at the margins."

Walker's preconceptions were most challenged by the young homeless, though he still thinks it was choice that put them on the streets. "They were forced out by a range of circumstances from violence, to rejection, to a breakdown of the family unit; or maybe the youngsters became too difficult to handle and were thrown out. Families have been destroyed by the removal of values and standards."

The choice in this case, he says, is made by parents who opt not to provide a suitable domestic environment for teenagers. But he claims to have identified young people who have chosen to go on the streets because it was a trendy thing to do.

"It has become fashionable and acceptable to sleep rough on the streets. It's almost a sub-culture, as if it was a macho cult to show that they could do it. They said they didn't want to enter into a disciplined, structured environment. Many of the youngsters had not applied for social security. They were living rough and begging and relying on food provided by voluntary bodies. One of them went so far as to say that you could live there forever without any money."

Walker's prescription? "There is ignorance and a lack of care and lack of standards. We've got to get a change of attitude which will require massive action from Parliament, the churches and all the opinion-formers. The role of the Salvation Army and people of that sort should be to bring their organisations into line with the demands and needs of today. I think that by constantly providing people with food and shelter at given times, they're actually encouraging homelessness. They should be concentrating their efforts and energies into improving the hostel structure."

Walker argues that the benefits system and the employment training programme need better targeting, for business too is seen to play a part in putting people on the streets. "They should be encouraged to provide hostels for young recruits, especially where accommodation prices are high."

HELP FOR STREET KIDS

"There are thousands of young Scots sleeping on the streets," said Glasgow MP, John Maxton. "To help them we should restore housing benefit for 16 and 17 year olds. There are also many empty properties which could be brought into use for the young homeless. We have to see that tenants who have bad landlords get good advice. And legislation on homelessness has to be tightened up to increase the numbers of those eligible for help."

HOMELESS PROJECTS GET £7·5 MILLION IN FUNDING

The Scottish Office is making £7·5m available to local authorities to fund 44 projects to tackle homelessness. The projects to be carried out will provide accommodation for about 700 homeless people. They include an emergency short-stay hostel in Glasgow and furnished tenancies in Edinburgh. Funding has also been made available to support single young people in Scottish cities who are homeless or at risk of becoming so.

The items here relate to the topic of homelessness among young people in Britain today. **Read them carefully.**

The material consists of the following:

  (i)   *Three newspaper articles;*

  (ii) *Definitions of homes and homelessness;*

  (iii) *Comments from young homeless people;*

  (iv) *Literature from* Shelter, *an organisation which campaigns on behalf of the homeless.*

Your task is to write a report on homelessness by selecting relevant information and reorganising the material in a way that shows an understanding of the main issues. You might find it helpful to consider the following:

  (*a*) what homelessness is;

  (*b*) the current problem and attitudes to it;

  (*c*) possible solutions.

You must base your report entirely on the material presented to you, and on any direct inferences you can draw from it. You should use your own words as far as possible. Remember you are asked to take an objective point of view. Write your report in formal, continuous prose. You are unlikely to be able to complete this task in fewer than 350 words.

(ii) *Defining homes and homelessness*

A home is a basic human need. It is more than just having a roof over your head. It is a place where you can bring friends and family, a place where you can feel secure, which you enjoy living in, somewhere of your own.

Shelter

rooflessness—perhaps the narrowest definition of homelessness is the one which equates homelessness with rooflessness—which describes the thousands of people who are sleeping rough in derelict buildings, barns, hedgerows, under the sky, wrapped in newspapers, old sacks and old clothes.

houselessness—a second, and in many ways more realistic definition of homelessness, is houselessness. This definition includes not only those who sleep rough, but also persons who occupy emergency accommodation which, for a limited period of time, provides special supportive resources, and other forms of short-stay or temporary accommodation.

Homelessness and the Law

(iii) *Comments from young homeless people*

"My mum's boyfriend hated me and didn't want me around so he told me to get lost. All I had was the clothes I stood up in but I tried to look clean by washing in pub toilets. I couldn't sleep at night because of the cold, so I'd keep walking till I got so many blisters on my feet I couldn't go any further."

Carol (18)

"I stayed in the inner city most of the time dodging the druggies. I slept in closes, anywhere really. I even slept in phone boxes bolt upright. At least I don't need an early morning alarm call! I've got my name down for a council flat which I'll share with my pal who's also on the streets. We're not looking for anything posh. The problem is that if you're 16 or 17 you can't get income support anymore. Before you could rent privately you needed a month's deposit and they used to give you that. But that's gone too. I just want somewhere of my own where I can feel safe."

Angela (16)

"You don't have any dignity left. If I hadn't been picked up by the police and taken to the hostel I don't think I'd be alive now. They helped straighten me out, and stopped me drinking."

Mark (18)

"I left home when I was 16. I'm happy the way I am. I manage to survive. I tap people in the street for money. But I'll maybe settle down and get married with kids sometime. I spend a lot of time at the Cyrenian Centre but there are only twelve beds and you can stay for only three months then you have to move on."

Annie (22)

(iv) *Literature from Shelter*

REASONS FOR HOMELESSNESS

The main reason people become homeless is that parents, friends or relatives can no longer put them up. They are often young people. They may have left home before but have not been able to find permanent accommodation of their own. Others have turned to relatives and friends following the breakdown of a relationship. With one in seven Scottish households overcrowded, it is not surprising that friends and relatives should eventually want to enjoy the privacy of their own homes. Neither is it unnatural that young people should leave home to begin lives of their own, but they should not be forced out by overcrowding or by family problems, leaving them with nowhere else to go.

LEGAL BACKGROUND

Since 1978, under The Housing (Homeless Persons) Act, councils have had a legal duty to provide advice, assistance and sometimes accommodation to homeless people. The Act makes a distinction between those who are in "priority need" and those who are not, and treats both groups differently. Some councils, but not all, include the under 18s in their priority group.

CONSEQUENCES

The massive increase in homelessness has resulted in the reappearance of landlords willing to make money out of people who have no home and no job. People without money have no bargaining power, so, if overcrowded or insanitary accommodation is offered, then they may have little choice but to accept it. The number of houses which have been turned into bedsits or "Bed and Breakfasts" has grown enormously, but the accommodation is often of a poor standard, overcrowded and very expensive. Yet the government, to keep people in such accommodation, is spending many millions of pounds which would be better invested in building decent, affordable homes. No matter how extortionate the rent, the tenants do not gain a single penny from the huge amounts of Housing Benefit being paid out. The landlords are the only winners. For tenants, all it buys is an insecure roof over their heads.

[END OF QUESTION PAPER]

SCOTTISH
CERTIFICATE OF
EDUCATION
1995

THURSDAY, 4 MAY
9.15 AM – 11.20 AM

ENGLISH
HIGHER GRADE
Paper I

There are **two parts** to this paper, Part 1 (Interpretation) and Part 2 (Report). You should attempt both parts.

Part 1 (Interpretation), on pages 2, 3 and 4, is worth 40 marks. There are two passages, with questions following. Use the left-hand margin of the answer book to indicate clearly the questions attempted.

Part 2 (Report), on pages 6, 7 and 8, is worth 35 marks. You should begin your Report on a fresh page of the answer book.

PART 1—INTERPRETATION

Attempt all of Part 1. You should spend approximately 1 hour on this part of the paper, including reading time. There are TWO passages and questions.

Read both passages carefully and then answer all the questions which follow on page four. **Use your own words whenever possible and particularly when you are instructed to do so.** The number of marks attached to each question will give some indication of the kind of answer required.

It is important that you read both passages before you attempt to answer any of the questions.

Passage 1 is taken from film critic Leslie Halliwell's The Dead That Walk, *his lively history of horror films. Passage 2 is part of a short story by Edgar Allan Poe (1809–1849), a famous American writer of horror fiction.*

PASSAGE 1

THE MENACE OF THE MUMMY

Boris Karloff once made some wise remarks about horror movies:

"Horror" means something revolting. Anybody can show you a pailful of innards. But the object of
5 *the roles I played is not to turn your stomach, but merely to make your hair stand on end. The descriptive word should have been "terror". They are bogey stories, that's all. Bogey stories with the same appeal as thrilling ghost stories or fantastic*
10 *fairy tales that entertain and enthral children in spite of being absurd.*

Certainly Karloff himself brought sympathy, even tragic stature, to his mad doctors and monsters; viewers were shocked by their plight
15 and relieved when their suffering was over. But he was set his most difficult task when Universal in 1932 decided to film *The Mummy*. A living 4000-year-old mummy, all earth mould and dirty bandages, is a pretty
20 loathsome concept, not a creature which even the most ardent horror fan can readily take to his heart.

Yet the fascination felt by frequent filmgoers for the details of Ancient Egyptian funeral
25 practices is the fulfilment of immemorial fantasies which still linger, however much sophisticated twentieth-century people, reading about how the Egyptians buried their dead 4000 years ago, may smile at the pious
30 beliefs involved. Not only the dead person's belongings but the body itself had to be preserved in the tomb for use in the after-life; though what use it could be is difficult to imagine, since the preservation process
35 involved the removal of most of the essential organs.

The remains were then anointed with soda and spices, the organs were separately wrapped, replaced within the body cavity, and the whole
40 was wound from head to toe in fine linen bandages. The rich and powerful dead had at least three coffins, one inside the other, and the outermost one sometimes of stone. The complete package was then reverently placed
45 in a secret rock chamber, and food and drink were left for the soul of the departed. Pharaohs were protected in enormous specially erected tombs called pyramids, the work of whole armies of slaves. There were trick entrances,
50 passages leading to dead ends, booby traps, and guards constantly on duty, all to fend off tomb thieves. Yet every precaution was largely in vain. Over the centuries all known tombs were plundered with the exception of that of
55 Tutankhamun. When his relics were discovered in 1922, they sparked off a world-wide interest in Egyptology, which Hollywood could not be expected to ignore.

The mummy films were never a major cycle—
60 women generally hated them—but they certainly scared the pants off plenty of boys of my generation—boys who had usually defied the Adults Only rule to huddle in a seat near the front and shudder as the ominous music grew
65 louder, and louder, and louder. The myth which Hollywood had developed for them naturally added a few elements to the known facts. In these films, by incantation or by the imbibing of a rare fluid, the half-preserved
70 shell of a 4000-year-old man was able to stagger to its feet and take violent revenge on all those who (a) plundered his tomb, (b) buried him alive, or (c) deprived him of his sweetheart. An element of reincarnation usually crept in, with
75 the mummy seeing in a modern young woman the soul of his ancient love and wanting to carry her back with him into eternity. (This was entirely out of place historically, since reincarnation was not among the many curious
80 beliefs of the Egyptians.) And although the mummy invariably moved as stiffly as the Tin Man before Dorothy found the oil can, no small-part actor was ever found who could move fast enough to get out of the way of this
85 foul accumulation of rotten bandages, its one good outstretched arm ending in a clawlike fist.

Nearly a hundred years before the discovery of Tutankhamun there had been stories about mummies, inspired no doubt by the many
90 Egyptian expeditions which brought back specimens to fill glass cases in eager museums around the world. Few will remember that Edgar Allan Poe wrote a mummy story, but he did . . .

PASSAGE 2

SOME WORDS WITH A MUMMY

Approaching the table, I saw on it a large box, or case, nearly seven feet long, and perhaps three feet wide, by two feet and a half deep. It was oblong—not coffin-shaped. The material was
5 at first supposed to be the wood of the sycamore (*platanus*), but upon cutting into it, we found it to be pasteboard, or, more properly, papier-mâché, composed of papyrus. It was thickly ornamented with paintings, representing
10 funeral scenes, and other mournful subjects— interspersed among which, in every variety of position, were certain series of hieroglyphical characters, intended, no doubt, for the name of the departed. By good luck, Mr Gliddon
15 formed one of our party; and he had no difficulty in translating the letters, which were simply phonetic, and represented the word, *Allamistakeo*.

We had some difficulty in getting this case
20 open without injury; but, having at length accomplished the task, we came to a second, coffin-shaped, and very considerably less in size than the exterior one, but resembling it precisely in every other respect. The interval
25 between the two was filled with resin, which had, in some degree, defaced the colours of the interior box.

Upon opening this latter (which we did quite easily) we arrived at a third case, also coffin-
30 shaped, and varying from the second one in no particular, except in that of its material, which was cedar, and still emitted the peculiar and highly aromatic odour of that wood. Between the second and the third case there was no
35 interval—the one fitting accurately within the other.

Removing the third case, we discovered and took out the body itself, and at this point it was agreed that we should experiment with the
40 Voltaic pile. Accordingly, an electric current was then applied to an incision in the tip of the mummy's nose.

Morally and physically—figuratively and literally—was the effect electric. In the first
45 place, the corpse opened its eyes, and winked very rapidly for several minutes, as does Mr Barnes in the pantomime; in the second place, it sneezed; in the third, it sat up on end; in the fourth, it shook its fist in Doctor
50 Ponnonner's face; in the fifth, it addressed them, in very capital Egyptian, thus—

"I must say, gentlemen, that I am as much surprised as I am mortified, at your behaviour. Of Doctor Ponnonner nothing better was to be
55 expected. He is a poor little fat fool who *knows* no better. I pity and forgive him. But you, Mr Gliddon—who have travelled and resided in Egypt until one might imagine you to the manner born—you, I say, who have been so
60 much among us that you speak Egyptian fully as well, I think, as you write your mother tongue—you, whom I have always been led to regard as the firm friend of the mummies—I really did anticipate more gentlemanly conduct
65 from *you*. What am I to think of your standing quietly by and seeing me thus unhandsomely used? What am I to suppose by your permitting Tom, Dick, and Harry to strip me of my coffins, and my clothes, in this wretchedly cold
70 climate? In what light (to come to the point) am I to regard your aiding and abetting that miserable little villain, Doctor Ponnonner, in pulling me by the nose?"

QUESTIONS FOR PART 1—INTERPRETATION

Questions on Passage 1

Marks

(*a*) "The descriptive word should have been 'terror'." (lines 6–7)

Using your own words, explain the distinction the actor Boris Karloff makes between "horror" and "terror". 2

(*b*) (i) What was unusual about Boris Karloff's playing of "mad doctors and monsters" (lines 13–14)? 2

    (ii) Why did the film, *The Mummy*, present him with his most difficult task? 2

(*c*) Explain fully, in your own words, the contrast Halliwell makes between "frequent filmgoers" (line 23) and "sophisticated twentieth-century people" (line 27). 4

(*d*) What picture of Ancient Egyptian society emerges from lines 41–52? 2

(*e*) Why do you think Hollywood could not be expected to ignore a world-wide interest in Egyptology? 2

(*f*) Re-read the first sentence of the fifth paragraph (lines 59–65). Comment on:

    (i) the different uses of dashes in lines 59–60 and line 62; 2

    (ii) the effect of the word "huddle" in line 63; 1

    (iii) the structure of the closing words: "as the ominous music . . . and louder." 1

(*g*) Hollywood "added a few elements to the known facts" (lines 67–68). Re-read carefully lines 65–86 and then, in your own words:

    (i) explain carefully what these new elements were; 3

    (ii) choose **two** of these elements and suggest—from your own knowledge— why they might have been added by the film-makers. 2

(23)

Questions on Passage 2

(*h*) The description of the "large box, or case" in the first paragraph is very detailed. Why do you think so much detail is given? 2

(*i*) The extract from Poe's short story falls into two quite different parts, the first ending at "the tip of the mummy's nose" (lines 41–42).

    (i) What is the difference in tone between the two parts? 2

    (ii) One word, in the first part of the passage, may clearly be seen as preparing the reader for the tone of the second part. Quote that word—and briefly justify your choice. 1

(*j*) Explain clearly what distinction is being made by the use of the words "figuratively" and "literally" in lines 43–44. 2

(*k*) By looking closely at the language used, show how Poe achieves humorous effects throughout the mummy's speech (lines 52–73). 4

(11)

Question on Both Passages

(*l*) Although both writers deal with the morbid topic of the mummy, their styles and tones are different.

By looking closely at style and tone, consider the differences and similarities in the two passages. 6

(6)

Total marks (40)

PART 2—REPORT

READ THE INSTRUCTIONS BEFORE YOU ATTEMPT THE QUESTION

(i) *Letters*

---

*How very much I enjoyed your article on women and food (*Living, *last week). I meet very few women who are able to get any enjoyment out of food. I see them at supermarket checkouts, sourly looking at their "diet" fizzy drinks, "virtually fat-free milk", and their bags of vegetables; or in restaurants, chomping through a salad and turning away the sweet trolley with a little cry of "Oh I mustn't!".*

It's as if enjoyment of food equals proof of appetite which equals lack of control which equals unfemininity. Only men, it seems, are allowed to tuck into a steak followed by steam pudding, without censure. I have never been on a diet. I think it is a waste of time—there's more to life than fitting in a size 12 dress.

LOIS STOCK
(size 14/16 and unrepentant)
Suffolk

It's now 22 weeks since I started to keep records of my diet. I'm very pleased to tell you that I'm about half-way there—I've lost 58lbs and six inches off each of my vital statistics. It hasn't been very difficult and many people have given me lots of encouragement. It even seems easy most of the time because I'm never hungry. I hope I really have changed some of my basic attitudes to food—only time will tell.

Psychologically, I suppose, it's a feeling of taking control that's important; after years of feeling unable or unwilling to tackle the problem it seems very liberating, strengthening, to be effecting change.

I should reach my goal soon and as things stand at present I can't imagine not doing it.

SUSAN WHITMORE,
Stoke-on-Trent

(ii) *Some information about our diet*

High levels of fat have been a feature of our diet since the Industrial Revolution. Fresh fruit and vegetables, with their short shelf-life, were virtually eliminated from the diets of most working-class Scots. The habit, now called "chip-pan cuisine", persists in many Scottish working-class areas today.

To Professor Robert Kendell, a chief medical officer, the effects are clear. "We have the highest mortality in the world from coronary artery disease and one of the highest cancer mortality rates. We also have a life expectancy which is less than that of Greece, which is a poorer country and has a worse health service. Our diet is a major worry, and fat is much more of a problem than either sugar or starch."

Although scientists are still unravelling the precise links between dietary fat and disease, the picture is becoming clearer. Medical studies have found that the population is getting fatter, with 40% of men and 25% of women overweight. One in ten of the population is considered to be obese. Obesity is the main cause of diabetes in middle-age, and can cause heart disease, gallstones and osteo-arthritis.

READ THIS SECTION BEFORE YOU ATTEMPT THE QUESTION

DIET

The items on pages 6, 7, 8, relate to the topic of Diet. Read them carefully.

Your task is to write a report on this topic by selecting relevant information and reorganising the material provided. You might find it helpful to consider the following:

    (*a*) problems caused by unhealthy eating habits;

    (*b*) current attitudes towards dieting;

    (*c*) possible solutions to the problems of over-eating.

You must base your report entirely on the material presented to you, and on any direct inferences you can draw from it. You should use your own words as far as possible. Remember you are asked to take an objective point of view. Write your report in formal, continuous prose. You are likely to be able to complete this task in about 400 words, but there is no penalty for exceeding this length.

You should spend approximately one hour on this part of the paper, which is worth 35 marks.

(iii) *Extract from Argyll and Clyde Health Board Survey*

HOW MANY PEOPLE ARE OVERWEIGHT?

There are no hard-and-fast definitions of overweight. We asked 2,200 people in the survey whether they thought they were underweight, about the right weight, or overweight. Here are their replies.

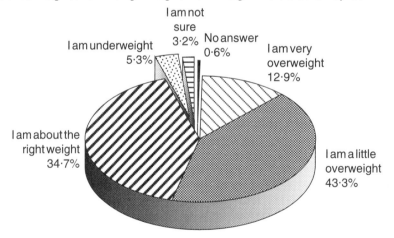

EXERCISE

The value of regular exercise is probably two-fold.

    * First, obesity (being seriously overweight) results from using up fewer calories through exercise than are taken in through eating. Regular exercise, together with a reduction in calorie intake, can therefore help people to keep their body weight within the normal range for their height, thus reducing the risk of diseases that are associated with obesity.

    * Second, people who exercise regularly may feel better and fitter than those who do not; they may enjoy more positive health, even though they may not have a markedly lower risk of disease.

(iv) *Newspaper Articles*

NUTRITION PUNDITS EAT THEIR WORDS

For the past 50 years a succession of dietary theories has been hurled at a largely unresponsive British public. Their contradictions have created confusion about what we should be eating, and why.

Polls show that the diet most firmly fixed in people's minds as healthy is generally the last but one to have been discredited. Many people, for example, still believe that bread, pasta, and potatoes are bad for you, a relic of the fifties' view that starchy foods were fattening and therefore unhealthy.

Today this wisdom has been reversed, with a series of official reports praising these foods as sources of fibre. High-fat foods have moved in the opposite direction, having been recommended in the late thirties by the nutritionist Lord Boyd-Orr as the cure for malnutrition, and damned in the eighties as the cause of heart disease. The evidence is that the food people eat has changed much less than the advice.

Nigel Hawkes

STORING UP TROUBLE

Last week a scare report appeared in the press that children as young as eight were becoming anorexic. Responsibility was lumped upon mothers who were constantly on diets and setting neurotic examples.

Experts at the Great Ormond Street Hospital for Sick Children in London, cited as the source of the story, have denied a rise in juvenile eating disorders, but it shows how conscious we are about weight and the problems it presents even to the young.

A fat child is often an unhappy child. A fat child is also an unhealthy child—one in five children is so overweight as to be at risk of heart disease, diabetes and high blood pressure in later life.

In a small proportion of children, physical and mental conditions can lead to obesity. Disorders of the thyroid or adrenal glands, tumours which may impinge on the brain's appetite centre, or even brain damage after an accident can all lead to overweight. GPs usually refer children to a paediatric clinic to check for disorders before considering a diet.

But that is a tiny number. For the rest, a host of reasons, from genes to gender, seems to play a part in determining which children get fat and which remain slim whatever they eat. Social circumstances also play a part—there are fewer obese children among the better educated and more affluent. Food abuse among the poor or the depressed could be stress- related, as food is frequently used as a tranquilliser.

Gender plays a part, too. Fewer boys than girls become or remain overweight. One reason is that their basal metabolic rate rises relative to their height, helping to burn off excess "puppy fat" as they grow.

Christine Doyle

CONFESSIONS OF AN UNJUSTIFIED GLUTTON

The doctors and the dieticians need a new approach. Get real, get tough; use words like "gluttony" instead of twee euphemisms. Personally, I would have appreciated less politeness. Not that I consulted a doctor—I remained fit, although nothing fitted. The main problem is that gluttony is the greatest convenience sin; much easier than the six other deadlies. It is readily available and perfectly legal—you don't have any problem getting fixes from pie dealers.

Educators are up against the really big one on gluttony. They are dealing with frightful self-deceivers. *You* are fat. *I* was only well built. At 5ft. 7in. I was perfectly proportioned (for 7ft. 5in.). "I eat very little but keep gaining weight" is the number one lie heard by dieticians.

The only way to slim is by cutting fat alone and, take it from me, the end does justify the jeans.

Dorothy-Grace Elder

[END OF QUESTION PAPER]

SCOTTISH
CERTIFICATE OF
EDUCATION
1995

THURSDAY, 4 MAY
2.10 PM – 3.45 PM

ENGLISH
HIGHER GRADE
Paper II

There are **two parts** to this paper and you should attempt both parts.

In Part 1, you should attempt **either** Section A (Practical Criticism) **or** Section B (Close Reading of Specified Texts).

In Section A there are two optional questions for Practical Criticism. If you choose Section A, attempt only one of the two Practical Criticism questions.

In Section B there are nine optional questions on Specified Texts. If you choose Section B, attempt only one of the nine Specified Texts questions.

Each option in Part 1 is worth 25 marks.

In Part 2 (Critical Essay), you should attempt **one** question only, taken from any of the Sections A–D.

Your answer to Part 2 should begin on a fresh page.

Each question in Part 2 is worth 30 marks.

NB You must not use, in any part of this paper, the same text(s) as you have used in your Review of Personal Reading.

You must also pay attention to the instruction at the top of each Section in Part 2 about the use of genres and specified texts.

Index of Specified Texts/Authors in Part 1 Section B

1 *Romeo and Juliet*
2 Robert Burns
3 *North and South*
4 *The Devil's Disciple*
5 *The Inheritors*
6 Iain Crichton Smith
7 *Death of a Salesman*
8 *Sunset Song*
9 Philip Larkin

PART 1

You should spend approximately 45 minutes on this part of the paper.

SECTION A—PRACTICAL CRITICISM

If you choose this Section, attempt <u>either</u> Option 1 below <u>or</u> Option 2, which begins on Page four.

Option 1

Enter the letter corresponding to each question in the left-hand margin of your answer book.

The passage below is taken from Robert McLellan's *Linmill Stories*, a collection of memories of the days spent at his grandfather's farm in Lanarkshire when he was a young boy. Here the author recalls an outing to the Clyde to catch "mennans" or minnows. The place was known as the "Lowp" or Leap because the river was so narrow there that it was possible to jump from one bank to the other.

Read the extract carefully and answer the questions which follow on **Page three**.

THE MENNANS

The wey ower the bank was gey kittle to tak, wi the rocks aa wat moss, and I grippit my grandfaither ticht, but he gat me to the bottom wi nae mair hairm nor the stang o a nettle on my left fute. He rubbit the stang wi the leaf o a docken, and tied a string to the neck o my jaur, and efter tellin me no to gang near the Lowp gaed awa back up to his wark.

5   An awesome laneliness came ower me as sune as he had turnt his back. It wasna juist the rummle o the Linn frae faurer doun the watter: it was the black hole aneth the bank at my back whaur the otters bade, and the fearsome wey the watter gaed through the Lowp. The front o the hole was hung ower wi creepers, and ye couldna be shair that the otters werena sittin ben ahint them, waitin to sneak oot whan ye werena lookin and put their shairp teeth into yer legs.

10   The Lowp was waur. It was doun a wee frae the otter hole, across a muckle rock, whaur the hail braid watter o Clyde, sae gentle faurer up, shot through atween twa straucht black banks like shinie daurk-green gless; and the space atween was sae nerra that a man could lowp across. It wasna an easy lowp, faur abune the pouer o a laddie, yet ye fand yersell staunin starin at it, fair itchin to hae a try. A halflin frae Nemphlar had tried it ance, in a spate whan the rocks were aa spume, and he had landit short

15 and tummlet in backwards, and it was nae mair nor a meenit afore his daith-skrech was heard frae Stanebyres Linn itsell, risin abune the thunner o the spate like a stab o lichtnin.

    The sun was oot, though, and I tried no to heed, and truith to tell gin it hadna been sae eerie it wad hae been lichtsome there, for in aa the rock cracks whaur yirth had gethert there were harebells growin, dentie and wan, and back and forrit on the mossie stanes that stude abune the watter gaed wee willie

20 waggies, bobbin up and doun wi their tails gaun a dinger, and whiles haein a douk to tak the stour aff their feathers.

    I didna gie them mair nor a look, for I had come to catch mennans, and as I grippit my can and jaur and gaed forrit ower the rock to the whirlies I could feel my hairt thumpin like to burst through my breist. It was aye the same when I was eager, and it didna help.

Marks

(*a*) By looking at the first sentence (lines 1–2), explain in your own words the circumstances in which the boy finds himself.   **2**

(*b*) When his grandfather departs, the boy is overcome with loneliness. By looking at the language of lines 5–9, consider how effectively the "awesome laneliness" of the young boy is conveyed.   **4**

(*c*) Read paragraph three (lines 10–16) again. Show how the dangers of the Lowp are made vivid in these lines by discussing:

    (i)   imagery;

    (ii) sound;

    (iii) sentence structure.   **6**

(*d*) (i)   Comment on the significance of the word "though" (line 17) at this point in the passage.   **2**

    (ii) By referring to the language of lines 17–21, show how the boy's mood is conveyed.   **5**

(*e*) By referring to particular features of the passage, consider to what extent the last paragraph (lines 22–24) is an effective conclusion to the extract.   **4**

(*f*) Select a word or phrase from the passage which you found particularly effective, and explain how it helped you to appreciate some aspect of the extract.   **2**

         (25)

SECTION A—PRACTICAL CRITICISM

Option 2

Enter the letter corresponding to each question in the left-hand margin of your answer book.

In this passage below from Neil Gunn's short story *The Tax-Gatherer*, a public official warns a woman that she will have to pay tax for the dog she keeps.

Read the extract carefully and answer the questions which follow.

The door stood half-open, stuck. He knocked on it and listened to the acute silence. He knocked again firmly and thought he heard thin whisperings. He did not like the hushed fear in the sounds, and was just about to knock peremptorily when there was a shuffling, and, quietly as an apparition, a woman was there.

5 She stood twisted, lax, a slim, rather tall figure, with a face the colour of the old limewash. She clung to the edge of the door in a manner unhumanly pathetic, and looked at him out of dark, soft eyes.

"Are you Mrs Williamson?"

After a moment she said, "Yes".

"Well, I've come about that dog. Have you taken out the licence yet?"

10 "No."

"Well, it's like this," he said, glancing away from her. "We don't want to get you into trouble. But the police reported to us that you had the dog. Now, you can't have a dog without paying a licence. You know that. So, in all the circumstances, the authorities decided that if you paid a compromise fine of seven-and-six, and took out the licence, no more would be said about it. You would not be taken to

15 court." He looked at her again, and saw no fewer than five small heads poking round her ragged dark skirt. "We don't want you to get into trouble," he said. "But you've got to pay by Friday—or you'll be summonsed. There's no way out."

She did not speak, stood there unmoving, clinging to the door, a feminine creature waiting dumbly for the blow.

20 "Have you a husband?" he asked.

"Yes," she said, after a moment.

"Where is he?"

"I don't know," she answered, in her soft, hopeless voice. He wanted to ask her if he had left her for good, but could not, and this irritated him, so he said calmly, "Well, that's the position, as you know. I

25 was passing, and, seeing we had got no word of your payment, I thought I'd drop in and warn you. We don't want to take you to court. So my advice to you is to pay up—and at once, or it will be too late."

She did not answer. As he was about to turn away, the dregs of his irritation got the better of him. "Why on earth did you want to keep the dog, anyway?"

"We tried to put him away, but he wouldn't go," she said.

30 His brows gathered. "Oh, well, it's up to you," he replied coldly, and he turned and strode back to his car. Slamming the door after him, he gripped the wheel, but could not, at the last instant, press the self-starter. He swore to himself in a furious rage. Damn it all, what concern was it of his? None at all. As a public official he had to do his job. It was nothing to him. If a person wanted to enjoy the luxury of keeping a dog, he or she had to pay for it. That's all. And he looked for the self-starter, but, with his

35 finger on the button, again could not press it. He twisted in his seat. Fifteen bob! he thought. Go back and slip her fifteen bob? Am I mad? He pressed the self-starter and set the engine off in an unnecessary roar. As he turned at the cross-roads he hesitated before shoving the gear lever into first, then shoved it and set off. If a fellow was to start paying public fines where would it end? Sentimental? Absolutely.

Marks

(*a*) Show by referring to two words or phrases in lines 1–4 how apprehension is conveyed when the tax-gatherer calls.

2

(*b*) Comment on the way in which two aspects of the woman's personality emerge in the description in lines 5–6.

2

(*c*) Explain what is revealed about the nature of the relationship between the tax-gatherer and the woman in lines 7–29 by referring to:

    (i) word choice;

    (ii) sentence structure;

    (iii) tone.

6

(*d*) How do any two of the man's actions in lines 30–32 reveal the range of his feelings?

4

(*e*) Choose one point in the extract at which the writer moves the reader from external events to the man's thoughts. Explain what is learned about the man at this point.

3

(*f*) Comment on the contribution of **each** of the following words to the overall impact of the passage:

    (i) summonsed (line 17);

    (ii) slip (line 36);

    (iii) cross-roads (line 37);

    (iv) absolutely (line 38).

8

(25)

SECTION B—CLOSE READING OF SPECIFIED TEXTS

If you have chosen to attempt this Section, you should select only ONE extract and answer the questions which follow it.

You should enter the number and the name of the text chosen at the top of the page, and the letter corresponding to each question in the left-hand margin.

You are reminded of the instruction on the front cover about the use of texts.

1. *ROMEO AND JULIET*

Read the extract carefully and answer the questions which follow. The number of marks attached to each question will give a clear indication of the length of answer required.

The dialogue below is taken from the beginning of Act II Scene 2 of the play.

	JULIET:	I would not for the world they saw thee here.
	ROMEO:	I have night's cloak to hide me from their eyes,
		And but thou love me, let them find me here.
		My life were better ended by their hate,
5		Than death proroguèd, wanting of thy love.
	JULIET:	By whose direction found'st thou out this place?
	ROMEO:	By love, that first did prompt me to inquire;
		He lent me counsel, and I lent him eyes.
		I am no pilot, yet wert thou as far
10		As that vast shore washed with the farthest sea,
		I should adventure for such merchandise.
	JULIET:	Thou knowest the mask of night is on my face,
		Else would a maiden blush bepaint my cheek,
		For that which thou hast heard me speak tonight.
15		Fain would I dwell on form, fain, fain deny
		What I have spoke; but farewell compliment.
		Dost thou love me? I know thou wilt say "Ay",
		And I will take thy word. Yet if thou swearest,
		Thou mayst prove false; at lovers' perjuries
20		They say Jove laughs. O gentle Romeo,
		If thou dost love, pronounce it faithfully.
		Or if thou thinkest I am too quickly won,
		I'll frown and be perverse, and say thee nay,
		So thou wilt woo; but else not for the world.
25		In truth fair Montague I am too fond,
		And therefore thou mayst think my 'haviour light.
		But trust me, gentleman, I'll prove more true
		Than those that have more cunning to be strange.
		I should have been more strange, I must confess,
30		But that thou overheard'st, ere I was 'ware,
		My true-love passion. Therefore pardon me,
		And not impute this yielding to light love,
		Which the dark night hath so discoverèd.

21

Marks

(a) Comment on the effectiveness of the imagery Romeo uses in explaining his situation (line 2).   **3**

(b) By close reference to the text, show how the language used in lines 7–11 reveals one aspect of Romeo's character.   **3**

(c)   (i) Trace the concerns which Juliet expresses in her speech:

"Thou knowest the mask . . .
My true-love passion." (lines 12–31)   **4**

  (ii) Go on to show how the sentence structure and tone used in these lines help to reveal Juliet's feelings.   **4**

(d) "Therefore pardon me,
And not impute this yielding to light love,
Which the dark night hath so discoverèd." (lines 31–33)

How effective do you find these lines as a conclusion to Juliet's speech?   **3**

(e) By looking briefly at the way Juliet is portrayed in this extract and more fully at another moment in the play, comment on the extent to which Juliet shows both youthful uncertainty and maturity of thought.   **8**

(25)

You are reminded of the instruction on the front cover about the use of texts.

2.   ROBERT BURNS

Read carefully the extract from *Holy Willie's Prayer* and answer the questions which follow. The number of marks attached to each question will give a clear indication of the length of answer required.

HOLY WILLIE'S PRAYER

<blockquote>
O THOU, wha in the Heavens dost dwell,
Wha, as it pleases best Thysel',
Sends ane to heaven and ten to hell,
  A' for Thy glory,
5 And no for ony guid or ill
  They've done afore Thee!

I bless and praise Thy matchless might,
Whan thousands Thou hast left in night,
That I am here afore Thy sight,
10 For gifts an' grace
A burnin' an' a shinin' light,
  To a' this place.

What was I, or my generation,
That I should get sic exaltation?
15 I, wha deserve most just damnation,
  For broken laws,
Sax thousand years 'fore my creation,
  Thro' Adam's cause.

When frae my mither's womb I fell,
20 Thou might hae plungèd me in hell,
To gnash my gums, to weep and wail,
  In burnin' lakes,
Where damnèd devils roar and yell,
  Chain'd to their stakes;

25 Yet I am here a chosen sample,
To show Thy grace is great and ample;
I'm here a pillar in Thy temple,
  Strong as a rock,
A guide, a buckler, an example
30 To a' Thy flock.
</blockquote>

Marks

(a) (i) Show how effectively the opening line sets the scene for the rest of the poem.   **2**

  (ii) By commenting on the first stanza, show clearly what impression you are given of Holy Willie's God.   **4**

(b) By close reference to stanzas 2–4, show the aspects of Willie's character that are revealed.   **4**

(c) Explain how, in the fifth stanza, the poet uses word choice and rhyme to expose the absurdity of Willie's beliefs.   **5**

(d) In the remainder of the poem, after this extract, Willie's hypocrisy is further revealed.

Choose an example of his hypocrisy and show how the language used helps to reveal this aspect of his character.   **4**

(e) "Holy Willie's Prayer" shows Burns the satirist. By making reference to two other poems by Burns, comment on the power of his comedy.   **6**

(25)

You are reminded of the instruction on the front cover about the use of texts.

3. *NORTH AND SOUTH*

Read the extract carefully and answer the questions which follow. The number of marks attached to each question will give a clear indication of the length of answer required.

The extract is taken from the chapter entitled "Dressing for Tea" in which Mr Thornton calls formally for the first time on the Hales.

She could hardly speak when she sat down at last, and told her mother that she was no longer Peggy the laundry-maid, but Margaret Hale the lady. She meant this speech for a little joke, and was vexed enough with her busy tongue when she found her mother taking it seriously.

"Yes! If anyone had told me, when I was Miss Beresford, and one of the belles of the county, that a
5 child of mine would have to stand half a day, in a little poky kitchen, working away like any servant, that we might prepare properly for the reception of a tradesman, and that this tradesman should be the only—"

"Oh, mamma!" said Margaret, lifting herself up, "Don't punish me so for a careless speech. I don't mind ironing, or any kind of work, for you and papa. I am myself a born and bred lady through it all,
10 even though it comes to scouring a floor, or washing dishes. I am tired now, just for a little while; but in half an hour I shall be ready to do the same over again. And as to Mr Thornton's being in trade, why he can't help that now, poor fellow. I don't suppose his education would fit him for much else." Margaret lifted herself slowly up, and went to her own room; for just now she could not bear much more.

In Mr Thornton's house, at this very same time, a similar, yet different, scene was going on. A large-
15 boned lady, long past middle age, sat at work in a grim handsomely-furnished dining-room. Her features, like her frame, were strong and massive, rather than heavy. Her face moved slowly from one decided expression to another equally decided. There was no great variety in her countenance; but those who looked at it once, generally looked at it again; even the passers-by in the street half-turned their heads to gaze an instant longer at the firm, severe, dignified woman, who never gave way in street-
20 courtesy, or paused in her straight-onward course to the clearly-defined end which she proposed to herself.

She was handsomely dressed in stout black silk, of which not a thread was worn or discoloured. She was mending a large, long table-cloth of the finest texture, holding it up against the light occasionally to discover thin places, which required her delicate care. There was not a book about in the room, with the
25 exception of Matthew Henry's Bible Commentaries, six volumes of which lay in the centre of the massive side-board, flanked by a tea-urn on one side, and a lamp on the other. In some remote apartment, there was exercise upon the piano going on. Some one was practising up a morceau de salon, playing it very rapidly, every third note, on an average, being either indistinct, or wholly missed out, and the loud chords at the end being half of them false, but not the less satisfactory to the performer.
30 Mrs Thornton heard a step, like her own in its decisive character, pass the dining-room door.

"John! Is that you?"

Her son opened the door, and showed himself.

"What has brought you home so early? I thought you were going to tea with that friend of Mr Bell's; that Mr Hale."

35 "So I am, mother. I am come home to dress!"

"Dress! Humph! When I was a girl, young men were satisfied with dressing once in a day. Why should you dress to go and take a cup of tea with an old parson?"

"Mr Hale is a gentleman, and his wife and daughter are ladies."

"Wife and daughter! Do they teach too? What do they do? You have never mentioned them."

40 "No, mother, because I have never seen Mrs Hale; I have only seen Miss Hale for half-an-hour."

"Take care you don't get caught by a penniless girl, John."

"I am not easily caught, mother, as I think you know. But I must not have Miss Hale spoken of in that way, which, you know, is offensive to me. I never was aware of any young lady trying to catch me yet, nor do I believe that anyone has ever given themselves that useless trouble."

45   Mrs Thornton did not choose to yield the point to her son; or else she had, in general, pride enough for her sex.

"Well! I only say, take care. Perhaps our Milton girls have too much spirit and good feeling to go angling after husbands; but this Miss Hale comes out of the aristocratic counties, where, if all tales be true, rich husbands are reckoned prizes."

50   Mr Thornton's brow contracted, and he came a step forward into the room.

"Mother" (with a short scornful laugh), "you will make me confess. The only time I saw Miss Hale, she treated me with a haughty civility which had a strong flavour of contempt in it. She held herself aloof from me as if she had been a queen, and I her humble, unwashed vassal. Be easy, mother."

Marks

(*a*)   How does Mrs Hale develop the idea of "Peggy the laundry-maid" in lines 4–7?   **2**

(*b*)   Compare and contrast the ways in which Mrs Hale and Margaret regard Mr Thornton. Refer to paragraphs 2 and 3 (lines 4–13) in your answer.   **4**

(*c*)   Consider paragraphs 4 and 5 (lines 14–30). Which of these two paragraphs provides a better introduction to Mrs Thornton? By referring closely to the language of each paragraph, give reasons for your choice.   **6**

(*d*)   Mrs Thornton is suspicious of people out of the "aristocratic counties" (line 48). Comment on the tone and implication of this phrase, and show how it is typical of her attitude throughout the whole novel.   **5**

(*e*)   Choose two scenes from later in the novel which involve John Thornton and Margaret Hale. Show how these scenes reveal a development in the relationship between the two characters.   **8**

(25)

You are reminded of the instruction on the front cover about the use of texts.

4.   *THE DEVIL'S DISCIPLE*

Read the extract carefully and answer the questions which follow. The number of marks attached to each question will give a clear indication of the length of answer required.

The following extract is taken from Act II of the play.

	THE SERGEANT:	Sorry to disturb you, mum. Duty! Anthony Anderson: I arrest you in King George's name as a rebel.
	JUDITH	[*pointing at Richard*]: But that is not — [*He looks up quickly at her, with a face of iron. She stops her mouth hastily with the hand she has raised to indicate him, and stands staring affrightedly.*]
5		
	THE SERGEANT:	Come, parson: put your coat on and come along.
	RICHARD:	Yes: I'll come. [*He rises and takes a step towards his own coat; then recollects himself, and, with his back to the sergeant, moves his gaze slowly round the room without turning his head until he sees Anderson's black coat hanging up on the press. He goes composedly to it; takes it down; and puts it on. The idea of himself as a parson tickles him: he looks down at the black sleeve on his arm, and then smiles slyly at Judith, whose white face shows him that what she is painfully struggling to grasp is not the humour of the situation but its horror. He turns to the sergeant, who is approaching him with a pair of handcuffs hidden behind him, and says lightly*] Did you ever arrest a man of my cloth before, Sergeant?
10		
15		
	THE SERGEANT	[*instinctively respectful, half to the black coat, and to Richard's good breeding*]: Well, no sir. At least, only an army chaplain. [*Showing the handcuffs*] I'm sorry sir; but duty —
	RICHARD:	Just so, Sergeant. Well, I'm not ashamed of them: thank you kindly for the apology. [*He holds out his hands.*]
20	THE SERGEANT	[*not availing himself of the offer*]: One gentleman to another, sir. Wouldn't you like to say a word to your missis, sir, before you go?
	RICHARD	[*smiling*]: Oh, we shall meet again before — eh? [*meaning "before you hang me"*]
	THE SERGEANT	[*loudly, with ostentatious cheerfulness*]: Oh, of course, of course. No call for the lady to distress herself. Still — [*in a lower voice, intended for Richard alone*] your last chance, sir.
25		

They look at one another significantly for a moment. Then Richard exhales a deep breath and turns towards Judith.

	RICHARD	[*very distinctly*]: My love. [*She looks at him, pitiably pale, and tries to answer, but cannot — tries also to come to him, but cannot trust herself to stand without the support of the table.*] This gallant gentleman is good enough to allow us a moment of leavetaking. [*The sergeant retires delicately and joins his men near the door.*] He is trying to spare you the truth; but you had better know it. Are you listening to me? [*She signifies assent.*] Do you understand that I am going to my death? [*She signifies that she understands.*] Remember, you must find our friend who was with us just now. Do you understand? [*She signifies yes.*] See that you get him safely out of harm's way. Don't for your life let him know of my danger; but if he finds it out, tell him that he cannot save me: they would hang him; and they would not spare me. And tell him that I am steadfast in my religion as he is in his, and that he may depend on me to the death. [*He turns to go, and meets the eyes of the sergeant, who looks a little suspicious. He considers a moment, and then, turning roguishly to Judith with something of a smile breaking through his earnestness, says*] And now, my dear, I am afraid the sergeant will not believe that you love me like a wife unless you give one kiss before I go.
30		
35		
40		

He approaches her and holds out his arms. She quits the table and almost falls into them.

| | JUDITH | [*the words choking her*]: I ought to — it's murder — |
| 45 | RICHARD: | No: only a kiss [*softly to her*] for his sake. |

JUDITH: I can't. You must —

RICHARD [*folding her in his arms with an impulse of compassion for her distress*]: My poor girl!

Judith, with a sudden effort, throws her arms round him; kisses him; and swoons away, dropping from his arms to the ground as if the kiss had killed her.

50 RICHARD [*going quickly to the sergeant*]: Now, Sergeant: quick, before she comes to. The handcuffs. [*He puts out his hands.*]

THE SERGEANT [*pocketing them*]: Never mind, sir: I'll trust you. You're a game one. You ought to a bin a soldier, sir. Between them two, please. [*The soldiers place themselves one before Richard and one behind him. The sergeant opens the door.*]

55 RICHARD [*taking a last look round him*]: Goodbye, wife: goodbye, home. Muffle the drums, and quick march!

The sergeant signs to the leading soldier to march. They file out quickly. . .

When Anderson returns from Mrs Dudgeon's, he is astonished to find the room apparently empty and almost in darkness except for the glow from the fire; for one of the candles has burnt out, and the other is at its last
60 *flicker.*

ANDERSON: Why, what on earth — ? [*Calling*] Judith, Judith! [*He listens: there is no answer.*] Hm! [*He goes to the cupboard; takes a candle from the drawer; lights it at the flicker of the expiring one on the table; and looks wonderingly at the untasted meal by its light. Then he sticks it in the candlestick; takes off his hat; and scratches his head, much puzzled. This*
65 *action causes him to look at the floor for the first time; and there he sees Judith lying motionless with her eyes closed. He runs to her and stoops beside her, lifting her head.*] Judith.

JUDITH [*waking; for her swoon has passed into the sleep of exhaustion after suffering*]: Yes. Did you call? What's the matter?

70 ANDERSON: I've just come in and found you lying here with the candles burnt out and the tea poured out and cold. What has happened?

JUDITH [*still astray*]: I don't know. Have I been asleep? I suppose — [*She stops blankly*], I don't know.

ANDERSON [*groaning*]: Heaven forgive me, I left you alone with that scoundrel. [*Judith*
75 *remembers. With an agonized cry, she clutches his shoulders and drags herself to her feet as he rises with her. He clasps her tenderly in his arms.*] My poor pet!

Marks

(a) Why does the sergeant, as he enters, mistake Richard for Pastor Anderson? 2

(b) Why does Richard not take the first opportunity which the sergeant gives him to speak privately to Judith? 2

(c) Consider the language which Richard uses in lines 28–42. Account for any differences which you notice between it and the language used in any other of Richard's speeches in the play. 6

(d) What motives do you think Richard has for insisting that Judith kiss him? 3

(e) Comment fully on Judith's line, "I can't. You must —" (line 46). 3

(f) What conclusion does Anderson jump to when Judith does not give a coherent answer to his question? (line 74) 1

(g) By looking closely at two occasions later in the play, show to what extent Judith's outlook altered because of Richard's actions in this scene. 8

(25)

You are reminded of the instruction on the front cover about the use of texts.

5.   *THE INHERITORS*

Read the extract carefully and answer the questions which follow. The number of marks attached to each question will give a clear indication of the length of answer required.

In Chapter 10, Lok and Fa find each other again after managing to avoid capture by the new people.

Fa's arms were up, her fists doubled, her teeth clenched, she was leaning and forcing her way through the water. They were still covered to the thigh when they clung to each other and made clumsily for the bank. Before they could see their feet again in the squelching mud Lok was laughing and talking.

"It is bad to be alone. It is very bad to be alone."

5   Fa limped as she held him.

"I am hurt a little. The man did it with a stone on the end of a stick."

Lok touched the front of her thigh. The wound was no longer bleeding but black blood lay in it like a tongue.

"It is bad to be alone — "

10   "I ran into the water after the man hit me."

"The water is a terrible thing."

"The water is better than the new people."

Fa took her arm from his shoulder and they squatted down under a great beech. The people were returning from the clearing with the second hollow log. They were sobbing and gasping as they went.

15   The two hunters who had gone off earlier were shouting down from the rocks of the mountain.

Fa stuck her wounded leg straight out in front of her.

"I ate eggs and reeds and the frog jelly."

Lok found that his hands kept reaching out and touching her. She smiled at him grimly. He remembered the instant connection that had made daylight of the disconnected pictures.

20   "Now I am Mal. It is heavy to be Mal."

"It is heavy to be the woman."

"The new people are like a wolf and honey, rotten honey and the river."

"They are like a fire in the forest."

Quite suddenly Lok had a picture from so deep down in his head he had not known it was there. For a
25   moment the picture seemed to be outside him so that the world changed. He himself was the same size as before but everything else had grown suddenly bigger. The trees were mountainous. He was not on the ground but riding on a back and he was holding to reddish-brown hair with hands and feet. The head in front of him, though he could not see the face was Mal's face and a greater Fa fled ahead of him. The trees above were flailing up flames and the breath from them was attacking him. There was
30   urgency and that same tightening of the skin — there was terror.

"Now is like when the fire flew away and ate up the trees."

The sounds of the people and their logs were far in the distance. Runners came thumping back along the trail to the clearing. There came a moment of bird-speech, then silence. The steps thumped back along the trail and faded again. Fa and Lok stood up and went towards the trail. They did not speak
35   but in their cautious, circling approach was the unspoken admission that the people could not be left alone. Terrible they might be as the fire or the river but they drew like honey or meat. The trail had changed like everything else that the people had touched. The earth was gouged and scattered, the rollers had depressed and smoothed a way broad enough for Lok and Fa and another to walk abreast.

"They pushed their hollow logs on trees that rolled along. The new one was in a log. And Liku will be
40   in the other."

Fa looked mournfully at his face. She pointed to a smear on the smoothed earth that had been a slug.

"They have gone over us like a hollow log. They are like a winter."

The feeling was back in Lok's body; but with Fa standing before him it was a heaviness that could be borne.

45 "Now there are only Fa and Lok and the new one and Liku."

For a while she looked at him in silence. She put out a hand and he took it. She opened her mouth to speak but no sound came. She gave a shake of her whole body and then started to shudder. He could see her master this shudder as if she were leaving the comfort of the cave in a morning of snow. She took her hand away.

50 "Come!"

Marks

(*a*) From Chapter 1 to Chapter 11, Golding lets us see the events of the story through the eyes of Lok. Provide from lines 3–31 any one example of how Golding continues to use this perspective, and explain briefly how he does so. **2**

(*b*) "The feeling was back in Lok's body; but with Fa standing before him it was a heaviness that could be borne." (lines 43–44)

This could suggest that Fa and Lok have not changed much from the characters they were in the first chapter of the novel.

   (i) By referring closely to their opening conversation (lines 4–12), explain to what extent you believe their characters have changed. **3**

   (ii) Read from "They pushed their hollow logs . . ." (line 39) down to the end of this passage. By close reference to the text, show to what extent this section provides further evidence for what you have said in your answer to (*b*)(i). **3**

(*c*) Fa's statement "I ate eggs and reeds and the frog jelly" (line 17) reminds us of the significance which Golding attaches to food in this novel. By referring to other parts of the novel, describe different ways in which food is given significance. **5**

(*d*) "Terrible they might be as the fire or the river but they drew like honey or meat." (line 36)

   (i) What impressions of the new people emerge from this particular extract? You should support your remarks with evidence from the passage. **4**

   (ii) By referring to other parts of the novel, explain to what extent you find that the above sentence from line 36 summarises the main problems which the arrival of the new people bring to Lok and his people. **8**

(25)

You are reminded of the instruction on the front cover about the use of texts.

6. IAIN CRICHTON SMITH

Read the poem carefully and answer the questions which follow. The number of marks attached to each question will give a clear indication of the length of answer required.

AT THE FIRTH OF LORNE

In the cold orange light we stared across
to Mull and Kerrera and far Tiree.
A setting sun emblazoned your bright knee
to a brilliant gold to match your hair's gold poise.

5   Nothing had changed: the world was as it was
a million years ago. The slaty stone
slept in its tinged and aboriginal iron.
The sky might flower a little, and the grass

perpetuate its sheep. But from the sea
10   the bare bleak islands rose, beyond the few
uneasy witticisms we let pursue
their desolate silences. There was no tree

nor other witness to the looks we gave
each other there, inhuman as if tolled
15   by some huge bell of iron and of gold,
I no great Adam and you no bright Eve.

Marks

(*a*) Re-read the first stanza.

    (i) What mood do you detect emerging from this stanza?

    (ii) How does the particular setting help in the creation of the mood?

    (iii) How do the mood and setting contribute to our understanding of the relationship of the couple?   **6**

(*b*) What significance do you see in the references to iron and gold in the poem as a whole?   **5**

(*c*) "Nothing had changed . . .
perpetuate its sheep." (lines 5–9)

By referring to the language of lines 5–9, show how the poet explores the idea that "nothing had changed".   **6**

(*d*) By referring to appropriate aspects of two other poems by Iain Crichton Smith, show how he explores the connections between individual people and the places in which they find themselves.   **8**

    (25)

You are reminded of the instruction on the front cover about the use of texts.

7.   *DEATH OF A SALESMAN*

Read the extract carefully and answer the questions which follow. The number of marks attached to each question will give a clear indication of the length of answer required.

In the following extract, Willy and Linda talk about finances while the presence of the Woman becomes obvious.

WILLY: I hope we didn't get stuck on that machine.

LINDA: They got the biggest ads of any of them!

WILLY: I know, it's a fine machine. What else?

5   LINDA: Well, there's nine-sixty for the washing-machine. And for the vacuum cleaner there's three and a half due on the fifteenth. Then the roof, you got twenty-one dollars remaining.

WILLY: It don't leak, does it?

LINDA: No, they did a wonderful job. Then you owe Frank for the carburettor.

WILLY: I'm not going to pay that man! That goddam Chevrolet, they ought to prohibit the manufacture of that car!

10   LINDA: Well, you owe him three and a half. And odds and ends, comes to around a hundred and twenty dollars by the fifteenth.

WILLY: A hundred and twenty dollars! My God, if business don't pick up I don't know what I'm gonna do!

LINDA: Well, next week you'll do better.

15   WILLY: Oh, I'll knock 'em dead next week. I'll go to Hartford. I'm very well liked in Hartford. You know, the trouble is, Linda, people don't seem to take to me.

   [*They move on to the forestage.*]

LINDA: Oh, don't be foolish.

WILLY: I know it when I walk in. They seem to laugh at me.

20   LINDA: Why? Why would they laugh at you? Don't talk that way, Willy.

   [*Willy moves to the edge of the stage. Linda goes into the kitchen and starts to darn stockings.*]

WILLY: I don't know the reason for it, but they just pass me by. I'm not noticed.

LINDA: But you're doing wonderful, dear. You're making seventy to a hundred dollars a week.

WILLY: But I gotta be at it ten, twelve hours a day. Other men — I don't know — they do it easier. I
25   don't know why — I can't stop myself — I talk too much. A man oughta come in with a few words. One thing about Charley. He's a man of few words, and they respect him.

LINDA: You don't talk too much, you're just lively.

WILLY [*smiling*]: Well, I figure, what the hell, life is short, a couple of jokes. [*To himself*] I joke too much! [*The smile goes.*]

30   LINDA: Why? You're —

WILLY: I'm fat. I'm very — foolish to look at, Linda. I didn't tell you, but Christmas-time I happened to be calling on F.H. Stewarts, and a salesman I know, as I was going in to see the buyer I heard him say something about — walrus. And I — I cracked him right across the face. I won't take that. I simply will not take that. But they do laugh at me. I know that.

35   LINDA: Darling . . .

WILLY: I gotta overcome it. I know I gotta overcome it. I'm not dressing to advantage, maybe.

LINDA: Willy, darling, you're the handsomest man in the world —

WILLY: Oh, no, Linda.

LINDA: To me you are. [*Slight pause.*] The handsomest.

40   [*From the darkness is heard the laughter of a woman. Willy doesn't turn to it, but it continues through Linda's lines.*]

LINDA: And the boys, Willy. Few men are idolized by their children the way you are.

   [*Music is heard as behind a scrim, to the left of the house, the WOMAN, dimly seen, is dressing.*]

WILLY [*with great feeling*]: You're the best there is, Linda, you're a pal, you know that? On the road —
45   on the road I want to grab you sometimes and just kiss the life outa you.

   [*The laughter is loud now, and he moves into a brightening area at the left, where the WOMAN has come from behind the scrim and is standing, putting on her hat, looking into a "mirror", and laughing.*]

Marks

(a) Identify one statement in the extract which confirms that the action takes place in Willy Loman's past and explain why it confirms the setting in time. **2**

(b) By referring closely to the extract, show how Willy's mood swings. (You might wish to refer to two of the following aspects: tone, word choice, and sentence structure.) **6**

(c) Examine in this extract the contribution made by two of the following features to the overall dramatic effect:

    (i) lighting;

    (ii) sound;

    (iii) movement;

    (iv) stage directions. **6**

(d) (i) What is the dramatic effect of the emergence of "*the WOMAN*" at the end of this extract? **3**

    (ii) Other minor characters in *Death of a Salesman* make an impact on the play as a whole. Describe in some detail two such characters and go on to explain their importance in the play. **8**

(25)

You are reminded of the instruction on the front cover about the use of texts.

8. *SUNSET SONG*

Read the extract carefully and answer the questions which follow. The number of marks attached to each question will give a clear indication of the length of answer required.

Chris attends her father's funeral.

      Uncle had come to her elbow then and he stood with her, the others stood back, it was strange and silent but for the soft patter of the rain on the yews and the Reverend Gibbon, shielding his Bible away from the wet drive of it, beginning to read. And Chris listened, her head bent against the rain's whisper, to the words that promised Resurrection and Life through Jesus Christ our Lord, who had died long syne
5   in Palestine and had risen on the third day and would take from that thing that had been John Guthrie quick, and was now John Guthrie dead, the quickness and give it habitation again. And Chris thought of her dream looking up at the coarse lands of the hills and thinking of the lands of death, was that where Christ would meet with father? Unco and strange to think, standing here in the rain and listening to that voice, that father himself was there in that dark box heaped with the little flowers that folk had sent,
10   father whom they were to leave here happed in red clay, alone in darkness and earth when the night came down. Surely he'd be back waiting her up in Blawearie, she'd hear his sharp, vexed voice and see him come fleetly out of the house, that red beard of his cocked as ever at the world he'd fought so dourly and well —

      Somebody chaved at her hand then, it was the grave-digger, he was gentle and strangely kind, and she
15   looked down and couldn't see, for now she was crying, she hadn't thought she would ever cry for father, but she hadn't known, she hadn't known this thing that was happening to him! She found herself praying then, blind with tears in the rain, lowering the cord with the hand of the grave-digger over hers, the coffin dirling below the spears of the rain. *Father, father, I didn't know! Oh father, I didn't KNOW!* She hadn't known, she'd been dazed and daft with her planning, her days could never be
20   aught without father; and she minded then, wildly, in a long, broken flash of remembrance, all the fine things of him that the years had hidden from their sight, the fleetness of him and his justice, and the fight unwearying he'd fought with the land and its masters to have them all clad and fed and respectable, he'd never rested working and chaving for them, only God had beaten him in the end. And she minded the long roads he'd tramped to the kirk with her when she was young, how he'd smiled at
25   her and called her his lass in days before the world's fight and the fight of his own flesh grew over-bitter, and poisoned his love to hate. *Oh father, I didn't know!* she prayed again, and then that was over, she was in the drive of the rain, hard and tearless, the grave-digger was pointing to the ground and she picked up a handful of soft, wet earth, and heard the Reverend Gibbon's voice drone out *Dust to dust, ashes to ashes,* and leant over the grave and dropped the wet earth; and then the grave-digger was
30   throwing in the turf, the coffin rang as though it were hollow, she stared at it till Uncle had her by the elbow, speaking to her, and so was the Reverend Gibbon but she couldn't hear them at first; and folk were to say she must have been real fond of her father after all, the best of a coarse bit family in the end.

Marks

(a) Briefly explain the circumstances which have led to Uncle Tam's prominence at the funeral.   **2**

(b) Comment on the significance of rain in the scene. You should consider closely two of the following references in your answer: lines 2–3; 16–18; 27–28.   **4**

(c) By referring to lines 3–13, show how the language conveys Chris's conflicting thoughts and emotions about death.   **4**

(d) Read lines 14–26 again ("Somebody chaved . . . *I didn't know!*").

  (i) From elsewhere in the novel, briefly explain one incident which has contributed to Chris's feeling that, "she hadn't thought she would ever cry for father" (line 15).   **1**

  (ii) By referring to sentence structure and word choice in lines 14–26, show how Chris's feelings about her father are revealed.   **6**

(e) To what extent do you consider John Guthrie to be an admirable figure in the novel? You should refer briefly to the extract and in detail to other parts of the novel in your answer.   **8**

    (25)

You are reminded of the instruction on the front cover about the use of texts.

9.   PHILIP LARKIN

Read carefully the extract from *The Whitsun Weddings* and answer the questions which follow. The number of marks attached to each question will give a clear indication of the length of answer required.

At first, I didn't notice what a noise
  The weddings made
Each station that we stopped at: sun destroys
The interest of what's happening in the shade,
5   And down the long cool platforms whoops and skirls
I took for porters larking with the mails,
And went on reading. Once we started, though,
We passed them, grinning and pomaded, girls
In parodies of fashion, heels and veils,
10   All posed irresolutely, watching us go,

As if out on the end of an event
  Waving goodbye
To something that survived it. Struck, I leant
More promptly out next time, more curiously,
15   And saw it all again in different terms:
The fathers with broad belts under their suits
And seamy foreheads; mothers loud and fat;
An uncle shouting smut; and then the perms,
The nylon gloves and jewellery-substitutes,
20   The lemons, mauves, and olive-ochres that

Marked off the girls unreally from the rest.
  Yes, from cafés
And banquet-halls up yards, and bunting-dressed
Coach-party annexes, the wedding-days
25   Were coming to an end. All down the line
Fresh couples climbed aboard: the rest stood round;
The last confetti and advice were thrown,
And, as we moved, each face seemed to define
Just what it saw departing: children frowned
30   At something dull; fathers had never known

Success so huge and wholly farcical;
  The women shared
The secret like a happy funeral;
While girls, gripping their handbags tighter, stared
35   At a religious wounding.

Marks

(a)   This extract itself starts at the third stanza of the poem. Describe briefly the mood created in the previous two stanzas of the poem.

2

(b)   Trace the references to "girls" throughout the extract and comment on Larkin's presentation of them.

4

(c)   What tone is created by lines 16–21? By referring closely to the language of these lines, explain how they create the tone you have identified.

4

(d)   Explain the oxymoron in "happy funeral" (line 33) and say how it helps your understanding of the scene.

2

(e)   "At first, I didn't notice what a noise
     The weddings made
Each station that we stopped at:"

What is the contrast between the speaker's initial reaction to the weddings in these lines (lines 1–3) and his reflection on the idea of marriage in general in the final two stanzas of the whole poem?

5

(f)   Choose another poem by Larkin which has as its subject matter the relationship between men and women. With close reference to the text, show how he treats this subject in the poem which you have chosen.

8

(25)

PART 2—CRITICAL ESSAY

Attempt ONE question only, taken from any of the Sections A to D.

In all Sections you may use Scottish texts.

You should spend about 50 minutes on this part of the paper.

Begin your answer on a fresh page.

If you use a Specified Text as the basis for your Critical Essay, you must not rely ONLY on any extract printed in Part 1 in this paper. If you attempt Section C—Poetry, you should note the additional instruction at the head of Section C.

SECTION A—DRAMA

> **If you have answered on a play in the Specified Text option in Part 1 of the paper, you must not attempt a question from this Drama Section.**
>
> **In your answer in this Section you should, where relevant, refer to such features as dialogue, characterisation, plot, theme, scene, climax, style, structure.**

1. "The abiding genius of Shakespeare is that he gives us characters about whom we care."

   By referring in detail to the actions and language of one character in a play by Shakespeare, explain to what extent you agree with the above comment.

2. With reference to a play which you have read or seen, describe the means used by the dramatist to depart from a realistic approach. Examine to what extent you believe the means used have contributed to the overall effect.

   (You may wish to refer to such things as the use of a chorus, or a narrator, or music, or a flexible time framework . . .)

3. "On stage, an open space which cries out for movement, the portrayal of youth is usually more successful than that of old age."

   Either

   (a) Examine the portrayal of an elderly character in a play which you have studied and assess to what extent his/her contribution to the play is important.

   Or

   (b) Examine the portrayal of the younger generation in a play which you have studied and assess to what extent you think the play succeeds in capturing the qualities associated with youth.

4. Where a play is to be staged — city theatre, studio theatre or village hall, for example — affects how it is to be staged. The director is thus presented with both opportunities and restrictions.

   With close reference to any play which you have read and seen, explain how you think the production was affected by the opportunities which the director chose to exploit, and/or the restrictions which he/she had to face.

5. Many dramatists explore the confrontation between opposing forces — for example: malice and kindness; dishonesty and integrity; cynicism and idealism.

   Examine how the confrontation between two opposing forces is treated in a play which you have studied.

SECTION B—PROSE

> **If you have answered on a prose work in the Specified Text option in Part 1 of the paper, you must not attempt a question from this Prose Section.**
>
> **In your answer in this Section you should, where relevant, refer to such features as setting, theme, characterisation, plot, content, style, structure, language, narrative stance, symbolism.**

6. "After hundreds of thousands of novels and short stories, there can be no new stories any more, only different treatments of the same broad themes . . ."

    With reference to any novel or short story, show how, though the theme might have been familiar to you, the novel or short story nevertheless led you to new insights.

7. The sea; farmed land; the hills; a city's streets; an imagined other world — often the setting of a prose work takes on an importance beyond that of simply providing the characters with a background against which to act out their lives.

    In any prose work which you have studied, show the importance of the writer's use of setting in the portrayal of character and/or action.

8. "A novel, to be truly successful, needs to combine both the local and the universal: it must speak truths in Edinburgh and Erinsborough, in Mollinsburn and Milan . . ."

    To what extent does a novel which you have read fulfil this traditional requirement — a successful novel should have both local and universal significance?

9. Some might argue that the popularity of travel writing is due to the fact that most readers do not travel; that biographies are popular because most people live uninteresting lives; and that the popularity of diaries is explained by readers' nosiness.

    How appropriate do you consider this comment to be with regard to any non-fiction text which you have read?

SECTION C—POETRY

> **If you have answered on a poem in the Specified Text option in Part 1 of the paper, you must not attempt a question from this Poetry Section. You may not base an answer on Burns's "Holy Willie's Prayer", Crichton Smith's "At The Firth Of Lorne" or on Larkin's "The Whitsun Weddings".**
>
> **In your answer in this Section you should, where relevant, refer to such features as rhyme, word-choice, language, sound, imagery, symbolism, style, structure.**

10. By referring closely both to the ideas and to poetic techniques in a poem which you know well, show whether or not your appreciation of the poem depends more on the ideas or on the techniques.

11. Poetry is often written as a result of reflecting on an intense emotional experience or on a significant event.

    Examine the techniques used by one poet to convey the significance of an experience or an event which gave rise to a poem or sequence of poems.

12. Poetry has been employed at times for very specific ends: to describe religious experience; to satirise; to record historical events; to flatter the rich and powerful; to be a form of propaganda or to tell a story . . .

    Choose a poem which in your view performs a specific "purpose"; show how the poet employs the poetic form in order to convey his/her ideas, beliefs or feelings.

SECTION D—MASS MEDIA

If your **Review of Personal Reading** is based entirely on a radio, television or film script, you must not attempt a question from this Mass Media Section.

13. Choose a film which contains a sequence of great power, excitement or tension. Briefly explain the context of the sequence in the film as a whole and go on to show how the effect is created. You should refer in your answer to mise-en-scène, montage and soundtrack.

14. Choose a film genre which has been consistently popular or one which is enjoying a revival. By referring in detail to such features as setting, heroes and villains, types of incident, social values, trends and tastes, account for the current success of the genre. You may wish to refer in your answer to two or more films or to one film in detail.

15. Choose a figure who, in your view, manipulates the media in order to construct a particular image. By closely referring to texts from more than one medium, explain the key features of this constructed image and show to what extent you consider it to be effective.

16. Choose a text which represents males and/or females in a way that provokes strong emotions in you. By closely referring to key elements of the text, explain your response.

17. Successful television drama series or serials are often based on occupational groups — the police, the armed forces, the fire-service, National Health Service workers, and so on.

Show to what extent the success of one series or of one serial depends on incidents which arise from the group's occupation or from the interplay of characters within the group.

(You may refer to one or more than one episode in your answer.)

18. Choose a play, series or serial which you enjoyed because the narrative is dominated by a powerful personality. Show how this domination is achieved. In your answer you may refer to such features as the character's role in the narrative, dialogue, appearance, camera techniques, choice of star, and so on ...

[END OF QUESTION PAPER]

SCOTTISH
CERTIFICATE OF
EDUCATION
1996

FRIDAY, 3 MAY
9.15 AM – 11.20 AM

ENGLISH
HIGHER GRADE
Paper I

There are **two parts** to this paper, Part 1 (Interpretation) and Part 2 (Report). You should attempt both parts.

Part 1 (Interpretation), on pages 2, 3 and 4, is worth 40 marks. There is one passage, with questions following. Use the left-hand margin of the answer book to indicate clearly the questions attempted.

Part 2 (Report), on pages 6, 7 and 8, is worth 35 marks. You should begin your Report on a fresh page of the answer book.

PART 1—INTERPRETATION

You should spend approximately 1 hour on this part of the paper, including reading time. There is ONE passage and questions.

Read the passage carefully and then answer all the questions which follow on page four. **Use your own words whenever possible and particularly when you are instructed to do so.** The number of marks attached to each question will give some indication of the kind of answer required.

Journalist Phil Reeves reports from New Mexico about a site which may remain contaminated for 10,000 years.

EARTHLINGS, KEEP OFF!

Most of the stuff earmarked for Waste Isolation Pilot Plant (WIPP) in the New Mexico desert is plutonium-contaminated detritus which emits relatively low quantities
5 of radioactivity—gloves, bits of drill, flasks, valves, rags, test-tubes, pipes, sludge, shoes, lab coats, and so on. But some of it is the most threatening material on earth. For this network of tunnelled-out salt corridors, 26
10 miles east of Carlsbad, is to become, if the US government has its way, home for all the radioactive garbage created by US weapons plants during the Cold War. This includes 24,000 soft steel 55-gallon caskets containing
15 waste that can kill someone within half an hour of exposure. The material will be radioactive for at least 10,000 years and, in some cases, far longer.

And therein lies the rub. Once the WIPP
20 complex is filled, sometime in the next 50 years, the plant above ground will be vacated and returned to the desert. Its small clump of sand-coloured administration buildings, surrounded by barbed wire, private guards,
25 and spotlights, will be removed.

How, then, should the rulers of today warn future generations of the filthy brew that they have buried beneath their feet? How will they stop them digging into it?

30 A response of sorts has come from the US Congress. As a condition for permitting the site to go ahead, it insisted that a warning sign should be erected when it closes down. This would have to be capable of alerting future
35 generations of the risk of opening up this unwanted tomb. It would be the most momentous "Keep Out" sign in history, a statement so forceful that it would drive people—or any other form of intelligent life—
40 away from the area until AD 12,000.

Yet this ruling raised more questions than it solved. How do you create a sign that is comprehensible over a hundred centuries? Why should anyone assume that it is possible
45 to create a structure that will outlive any previous empire—from Mongolian and Ming to Roman and Russian? It is not as

if the meaning of Stonehenge, which is a mere 3,500 years old, is crystal clear to modern man.

50 And how do you physically go about building something that can survive for so long, without being destroyed by sandstorms, or tumbled by an earthquake, let alone nuclear war? Of the original Seven Wonders of the World, only one
55 still stands—Khufu's pyramid at Giza in Egypt.

Nor is it easy to see how you ensure that any sizeable monument, however forbidding, will not fill gold-diggers or future archaeologists
60 with such curiosity that they start digging underneath it. Over the ages, few historic sites have been spared intrusion from bounty-hunters, vandals or prying scholars. Worse, the dump lies in an area of south-eastern New
65 Mexico which is dotted with oil and hydrogen wells, and basalt mines. A prospector could happen upon its contents while boring for minerals.

To tackle these issues, the Sandia National
70 Laboratory in Albuquerque, the nuclear weapons development and research agency which is overseeing the project for the US Department of Energy, convened a panel of 13 experts. They included anthropologists,
75 materials scientists, astronomers, a psychologist, an architect and a linguist. Their deliberations were closely followed by nuclear regulatory agencies worldwide, including Britain's. It was the first time anyone, anywhere, had explored
80 the issue in such detail.

The panel divided into two teams. One offered a number of alternatives. These included: a "Landscape of Thorns"—a square mile of randomly-spaced 80ft basalt spikes which
85 jut out of the ground at different angles; "Menacing Earthworks"—giant mounds surrounding a 2,000ft map of the world displaying all the planet's nuclear waste dumps; a "Black Hole"—a huge slab of black
90 concrete that absorbs so much solar heat that it is impossible to approach.

The second team favoured a field of 50ft granite obelisks (Washington Monument-style

structures that would be large enough not
95 to be buried by sand dunes). Beneath the earth,
there would be further warning emblems in
case someone made off with the surface
monuments, just as they did in the past with
Cleopatra's Needles. There would also be a
100 device to ensure that the site showed up on
radar.

"We toyed with the idea of actually burying
some treasure 20 feet down so that anyone
digging would think that they had found
105 whatever they were looking for," said Professor
Frank Drake, an astrophysicist from the
University of California, "but we dismissed
that as too kooky. There was a lot of discussion
about the morality of the whole thing. At one
110 stage we thought that the site should not be
marked at all, but we decided that that was
unethical."

The panellists put forward proposals for
figurative warnings—cartoons showing a stick
115 figure collapsing from the effects of radiation,
or a contorted face like Munch's *The Scream*.
They also recommended written messages—
lengthy explanations of the dump's contents in
English, French, Arabic, Russian, Chinese,
120 Spanish and possibly the language of the local
Mescalero Apache Indians.

The final decision about what to erect will
take some time. At the moment the WIPP
project has been held up in the federal courts by
125 a series of lawsuits over the safety of its
operation, filed by environmental groups and
the state of New Mexico.

But few doubt that the lorries (on average five a
day) of nuclear-poisoned trash will eventually
130 start rumbling across the southern desert,
laden with waste destined for the ancient
seabed. The US government is unlikely to
abandon its newly-dug underworld. They
drilled 2,150ft into the ground to build it, and
135 they have already spent $1·5bn on the project.

The effectiveness of the so-called "Sign of the
Ages" to warn the heirs to the planet away from
their unwanted inheritance remains in doubt.
It is hard to believe that, however expert the
140 Americans claim to be, they have the slightest
idea of how their utterances will be received in
200 years' time, let alone in another epoch.

The day after visiting WIPP, I flew back to Los
Angeles. My taxi driver at the airport was from
145 Lithuania, an erstwhile resident of the "evil
empire" that helped to generate the US nuclear
weapons. I asked him to go to Encino, the
neighbourhood where I live. "Cinema?" he
replied. I tried signs and gestures. Only after
150 15 minutes of garbled conversation did we
straighten matters out. What chance would we
have had, separated by 10,000 years?

QUESTIONS FOR PART 1—INTERPRETATION

Marks

(a) Show how the first sentence (lines 1–7) provides a context which enables you to understand the meaning of the word "detritus" (line 4). **2**

(b) "And therein lies the rub." (line 19)

Explain how this sentence acts as a link between the first paragraph and the two following paragraphs. **2**

(c) Explain how effective you find the metaphor "filthy brew" (line 27). **2**

(d) "A response of sorts has come from the US Congress." (lines 30–31)

What does this sentence suggest about the writer's attitude to the response, and how does it do so? **2**

(e) How is the idea contained in the word "momentous" (line 37) developed in the rest of that sentence? **2**

(f) Paragraphs 5, 6 and 7 (lines 41–68) deal with the "issues" referred to in line 69.

In your own words, describe clearly what the three main issues are. **6**

(g) Choose any **two** of the experts referred to in lines 74–76, and explain the probable usefulness of each of these experts to the project. **2**

(h) Show how the punctuation of lines 82–91 is particularly helpful in following the argument at this stage. **3**

(i) By commenting on specific words and/or phrases in paragraph 11 (lines 102–112), show to what extent you would have confidence in Professor Frank Drake and his team. **4**

(j) (i) What would be an advantage of the "figurative warnings" mentioned in line 114? **1**

   (ii) Which single word in paragraph 10 (lines 92–101) prepares us for this proposal? **1**

(k) ". . . and possibly the language of the local Mescalero Apache Indians." (lines 120–121) Comment as fully as you can on the significance of these words as a conclusion to paragraph 12. **3**

(l) By commenting on particular words or phrases from paragraphs 13–15 (lines 122–142), show how the writer conveys a sense of the dramatic nature of the whole project. **4**

(m) By referring to the incident which is described in the final paragraph, show how it is important in **two** ways to the passage as a whole. **4**

(n) In the light of your understanding of the whole passage, explain how appropriate you consider the title of the passage, "EARTHLINGS, KEEP OFF!". **2**

Total marks (40)

PART 2—REPORT

READ THE INSTRUCTIONS BEFORE YOU ATTEMPT THIS QUESTION

(i)

The Problem with Pop

The three young girls and the boy are on stage at King Tut's Wah Wah Hut in Glasgow and the small club is mobbed. The mood ought to be infectious, but the sad fact is that Elastica is the latest in a now embarrassing line of British bands to have the "buzz" thrust upon them. Elastica have featured on the front covers of national music papers. They won the Most Promising Newcomer award in the *New Musical Express*. They are, we are asked to believe, Britain's future in the world of popular music.

Yet Elastica have released only one proper single to date. It's good but that's all. The emperor's new clothes are wearing thin when we are told that this competence has to be received as brilliance by everyone. There is an air of desperation about. Anyone and everyone is seen as the next best thing when they have barely learned to pluck a guitar string.

So what's going wrong? On the face of it, the industry is buoyant enough. 56 million singles are sold in Britain each year; higher than throughout the Sixties and Seventies. Yet a number one single will, on average, now sell only 59,000 copies in total. That's less than £150,000 to become a household name. Overall we may be buying more music, but now we rarely like the same things. The comfortable consensus ironically remembered as the Pop Revolution has become a thing of the past.

Pop stars may still be with us for a while yet, but there is no mistake, we are at the end of an era. Future historians will look back and see the phenomenon that was "pop music" perfectly preserved in a four-decade span, from the sixties to the nineties. The credo of popular music was live fast, die young.

Now it has!

(ii)

Letter to the Press

Pop is dead? Try telling that to the readers of *Smash Hits* magazine, who write 1,000 letters to it every week. Let's not kid ourselves, Pop's not really dying . . . it's just reacting to the time it's existing in. Just as it has always done; just as all organic things do.

That pop music just isn't what it used to be is an argument I'm sick of hearing from ageing newspaper columnists. When exactly was the golden age, when we all listened to the same supergroups, that they all seem to remember? Twenty years ago Mud were at number one with, wait for it, the Wombles not far behind. Sounds great, man!

Pop has grown from its humble beginnings and has become a multi-billion, multi-media, multi-entertainment industry. Pop is dead? Pop will never die. Yes it will change. It is youthful and fashionable and open to change. Quite unlike the people who write about it in the newspapers!

Record Promoter

The items on pages 6, 7, 8, relate to the topic of popular music in Britain. Read them carefully.

The material consists of the following:

(i) Article entitled "The Problem with Pop";

(ii) Letter to the Press;

(iii) Extract entitled "Cultural Heritage";

(iv) Article entitled "Sound and no vision";

(v) Extract entitled "Nature of Pop Music";

(vi) Some brief views about Pop Music.

Your task is to write a report on the development and current state of popular music by selecting relevant information and reorganising the material in a way that shows an understanding of the main issues. You might find it helpful to consider the following:

(*a*) brief definition of pop music and its importance in Britain;

(*b*) concerns about its current state;

(*c*) reactions to such concerns.

You must base your report entirely on the material presented to you, and on any direct inferences you can draw from it. You should use your own words as far as possible and write your report in formal, continuous prose. You are unlikely to be able to complete this task in fewer than 400 words.

You should spend approximately one hour on this part of the paper, which is worth 35 marks.

(iii)

Cultural Heritage

Pop music is Britain's last great bastion of cultural imperialism, or contribution to the global village, depending on where you stand. We virtually invented it with The Beatles, The Rolling Stones, The Who and The Kinks. If we don't worry about our position as cultural leaders of the world in this field, it's because we don't have to. Britain has been dominating pop culture for much of the last 30 years.

(iv)

Sound and no vision

The trouble with pop music, we are constantly assured, is that it has stopped being truly popular. Every other week you can read the obituaries. They have become one of the great journalistic cliches of our time. A couple of weeks ago, that normally unfaddish journal *The Spectator* joined in, suggesting that not only were we not all singing from the same hymn sheet any more, but that "popular culture no longer exists". The idea here is that pop music has lost its centrality and hence forfeited its validity because we have all got so many other things to do. The buzzword is "fragmentation".

This doctrine states that once upon a time we all loved The Beatles or Cliff Richard, or somebody. Nowadays, none of us likes, or possibly even recognises, each other's idols.

The fragmentation doctrine, however, certainly contains some hefty mythical elements. That golden age when we sang and listened as one, for instance, has never existed in my lifetime. The tribal separation of pop tastes in the 1960s was as profound as any of today's stand-offs.

In 1967, a year we now cherish for Sgt Pepper and flower power, the biggest hit records were two sentimental ballads, *The Green Green Grass of Home* and *Release Me*, sung by a couple of smoothly coiffeured crooners who looked like nightclub doormen (Tom Jones and Engelbert Humperdinck). The contempt and loathing inspired by these tracks makes the recent row about Mr Blobby's musical credentials look polite by comparison. Today's pop historians would have us believe that pop music has ceased to supply an adequate soundtrack to the time; ceased to unite us behind one dominant form of pop music. Well, rubbish to that! We have never had, nor would we want to have, a total consensus about musical taste.

(v)

Nature of Pop Music

Pop music is best defined as music created for a mass audience, and is marketed accordingly by the record industry. Pop records get the bulk of the attention of the advertisers, distributors and retailers. Over the last 30 years, pop has become the most pervasive form of popular culture and the most prosperous part of the entertainment industry.

(vi)

Some Brief Views About Pop Music

Raves are Killing British Pop

In the late 1980s raves fuelled a massive explosion in British youth culture. It's difficult to over-emphasise its size and effect. Raves in the middle of nowhere attracted thousands of dancers. The popularity of raves has meant a shrinking audience for pop groups trying to make their marks.

Pop's Too Old

Just look at the stars: most of them are ancient. Rod Stewart, Mick Jagger, David Bowie, Elton John, Phil Collins . . . they refuse to roll over, and the ageing audience shows no signs of letting them go. Musically, they're obsessed with the past . . .

Computer Games Threat To Pop

Teenagers, hard though it is to believe, are bored with Pop. The music industry, whose very life blood has been, until now, a succession of unhealthy teenage cravings, has found itself upstaged. Video games have spread across the nation's playgrounds like lice. At this moment, an estimated five million handsets are being squeezed by frenzied British adolescents. The video games business is worth £500 million a year. Although it is generally agreed that parents stump up most of the cost, games have made a hole in the cash available to buy records. Sales of singles and albums have dropped dramatically.

Singles To Go

The single is fast reaching the end of the track. Record companies are abandoning the format that has dominated pop music for more than 40 years and launched dozens of international stars from The Beatles to George Michael. EMI and Sony, two of the biggest firms, are to stop issuing singles in Britain for many artists because of low sales and volatile charts. It will hasten the end for the medium that made pop music affordable and turned it into an international language.

[END OF QUESTION PAPER]

SCOTTISH
CERTIFICATE OF
EDUCATION
1996

FRIDAY, 3 MAY
2.10 PM – 3.45 PM

ENGLISH
HIGHER GRADE
Paper II

There are **two parts** to this paper and you should attempt both parts.

In Part 1, you should attempt **either** Section A (Practical Criticism) **or** Section B (Close Reading of Specified Texts).

In Section A there are two optional questions for Practical Criticism. If you choose Section A, attempt only one of the two Practical Criticism questions.

In Section B there are nine optional questions on Specified Texts. If you choose Section B, attempt only one of the nine Specified Texts questions.

Each option in Part 1 is worth 25 marks.

In Part 2 (Critical Essay), you should attempt **one** question only, taken from any of the Sections A–D.

Your answer to Part 2 should begin on a fresh page.

Each question in Part 2 is worth 30 marks.

NB You must not use, in any part of this paper, the same text(s) as you have used in your Review of Personal Reading.

You must also pay attention to the instruction at the top of each Section in Part 2 about the use of genres and specified texts.

Index of Specified Texts/Authors in Part 1 Section B

1 *Romeo and Juliet*
2 Robert Burns
3 *North and South*
4 *The Devil's Disciple*
5 *The Inheritors*
6 Iain Crichton Smith
7 *Bold Girls*
8 *Sunset Song*
9 Philip Larkin

PART 1

You should spend approximately 45 minutes on this part of the paper.

SECTION A—PRACTICAL CRITICISM

If you choose this Section, attempt either Option 1 below or Option 2, which begins on Page four.

Option 1

Enter the letter corresponding to each question in the left-hand margin of your answer book.

In *The Quarry Wood*, the author Nan Shepherd tells how Mrs Emmeline Ironside and Miss Josephine Leggatt came to agree that Mrs Ironside's young daughter Martha should go to stay with Miss Josephine, her grand-aunt, at Crannochie.

Read the extract carefully and answer the questions which follow on **Page three**.

Martha Ironside was nine years old when she kicked her grand-aunt Josephine. At nineteen she loved the old lady, idly perhaps, in her natural humour, as she loved the sky and space. At twenty-four, when Miss Josephine Leggatt died, aged seventy-nine and reluctant, Martha knew that it was she who had taught her wisdom; thereby proving—she reflected—that man does not learn from books alone
5 because Martha had kicked Aunt Josephine (at the age of nine) for taking her from her books.

Mrs Ironside, to be sure, had a dozen reasons against taking the child away from school. Reasoning to Miss Leggatt was so much moonshine. Fretful little girls are solid realities (if not so solid as their grand-aunts might wish): reasons, merely breath. It was not to be expected that a vapour would impede Aunt Josephine. She announced calmly and conclusively that she was taking the child back with
10 her to Crannochie.

"We'll just cry on the craitur," she said, "and lat her know."

The *craitur* all this while, serenely unaware of the conspiracy against her peace, was dwelling on a planet of her own. A field's breadth from the cottage, where two dykes intersected, there was piled a great cairn of stones. They had lain there so long that no one troubled to remember their purpose or
15 their origin. Gathered from the surrounding soil, they had resumed a sort of unity with it. The cairn had settled back into the landscape, like a dark outcrop of rock. There Martha played. The stones summed up existence.

"She's just a skin," said Miss Leggatt, pausing at the foot of the cairn, while Mrs Ironside's voice came spattering past her in little bursts:
20 "Tak yer hair ooten yer mou', Matty . . . and say how-do-you-do . . . to yer aunt. Mumblin' yer hair . . . like that . . . I never saw the like."

"She's hungry, that's fat she is, the littlin," said Aunt Josephine. "Ye're fair hungerin' her, Emmeline." And she put out her hands and drew Martha towards her by the shoulders. "Now, my dear," she said. It was a finished action and a finished phrase. Miss Leggatt's simplest word had a way
25 of suggesting completion, as though it conveyed her own abounding certainty in the rightness of everything.

Emmeline told her daughter what was in store for her.

"Wunna that be fine?" said Aunt Josephine.

Martha, firmly held by the shoulders in Aunt Josephine's grasp, answered by the action and not by
30 word. Words came slowly to her need; and her present need was the most unmanageable she had ever experienced; for school to Martha was escape into a magic world where people knew things. Already she dreamed passionately of knowing all there was to know in the universe: not that she expressed it so, even to herself. She had no idea of the spaciousness of her own desires; but she knew very fervently that she was in love with school. Her reaction to the news she had just heard, therefore, was in the nature of
35 protest—swift and thorough. She simply kicked out with all her strength of limb.

"I wunna be ta'en awa fae the school," she screamed. "I wunna. I wunna."

"Did ever ye see the likes o' that?" panted her mother. "Be quaet, will ye, Matty? I'm black affronted at ye. Kickin' yer aunt like that. Gin I cud get ye still a meenute, my lady, I'd gar yer lugs hotter for ye."
40 Martha kicked and screamed the more.

Aunt Josephine let them bicker. Troubling not even to bend and brush the dust of Martha's footmarks from her skirt, she walked back calmly to the cottage.

Marks

(a) In the first paragraph (lines 1–5), the narrator summarises Martha's changing feelings toward her grand-aunt Josephine.

   (i) Say, in your own words, how her feelings changed as she grew older.   **3**

   (ii) Show how the structure of the sentences in the first paragraph reinforces her changing feelings.   **4**

(b) Show how the author uses two of the following techniques in the second paragraph (lines 6–10) to develop the character of Martha's grand-aunt Josephine, Miss Leggatt:

   (i) word choice;

   (ii) sentence structure and punctuation;

   (iii) contrast.   **4**

(c) (i) Show how the writer evokes sympathy for Martha in paragraph four (lines 12–17).   **2**

   (ii) Comment on the effectiveness of the imagery of the final sentence, "The stones summed up existence" (lines 16–17), in helping you to understand Martha's situation.   **2**

(d) Show how the contrast between Aunt Josephine and Mrs Ironside is further developed from line 18 to the end of the extract. You should refer to dialogue, action, and word choice.   **6**

(e) This extract is from the opening chapter of a novel. Say briefly what you think the novel might be about in terms of plot and ideas and go on to justify your statements by close reference to this extract.   **4**

   (25)

Option 2

Enter the letter corresponding to each question in the left-hand margin of your answer book.

Read the poem carefully and answer the questions which follow on **Page five**.

WAITING ROOM

She waits neatly, bone-china thin,
in a room tight with memories,
claustrophobic with possessions,
rendered down from eighty years,
5   eight Homes and Gardens rooms.

She waits graciously, bearing
the graffiti of age. She drizzles
sherry into fine glasses, tea
into what is left
10   of wide-brimmed wedding china.

With the top of her mind
she is eager to skim off news
of the family, who married whom
and when. Names elude her. Tormented,
15   she tries to trap them on her tongue.

She waits defiantly, fumbling
to light a cigarette, veins
snaking across her hands
like unravelled knitting. A man's face,
20   preoccupied by youth, looks on.

We leave her, the stick a third leg,
waiting to obey the gong,
(Saturday, boiled eggs for tea)
waiting for the rain to stop,
25   waiting for winter, waiting.

Moira Andrew

Marks

(a)   (i) By referring to the language in the first line, state what initial impression of the woman is conveyed.   **2**

    (ii) Go on to explain how the poet's choice of details in the lines 2–9 helps you to appreciate the changes that have taken place in the woman's circumstances over the years.   **6**

(b) Stanzas three and four (lines 10–18) reveal other aspects of the woman. By referring to such features as sentence structure, poetic techniques, point of view, tone, show how these aspects are conveyed.   **6**

(c)   (i)   "A man's face,
preoccupied by youth, looks on." (lines 19–20)

Comment on the significance for you of these lines in the context of the whole poem.   **2**

    (ii) From an examination of the poet's use of language and choice of details in the first four stanzas, show how sympathy is elicited for an old woman.   **3**

(d) Trace the development of the idea of "waiting" throughout the poem and comment on the significance of that idea.   **6**

    (25)

SECTION B—CLOSE READING OF SPECIFIED TEXTS

If you have chosen to attempt this Section, you should select only ONE extract and answer the questions which follow it.

You should enter the number and the name of the text chosen at the top of the page, and the letter corresponding to each question in the left-hand margin.

You are reminded of the instruction on the front cover about the use of texts.

1. *ROMEO AND JULIET*

Read the extract carefully and answer the questions which follow. The number of marks attached to each question will give a clear indication of the length of answer required.

This extract is taken from Act V Scene 3 of the play.

	ROMEO:	How oft when men are at the point of death
		Have they been merry, which their keepers call
		A lightning before death. O how may I
		Call this a lightning? O my love, my wife!
5		Death that hath sucked the honey of thy breath,
		Hath had no power yet upon thy beauty.
		Thou art not conquered; beauty's ensign yet
		Is crimson in thy lips and in thy cheeks,
		And death's pale flag is not advanced there.
10		Tybalt, liest thou there in thy bloody sheet?
		O what more favour can I do to thee,
		Than with that hand that cut thy youth in twain
		To sunder his that was thine enemy?
		Forgive me, cousin. Ah, dear Juliet,
15		Why art thou yet so fair? Shall I believe
		That unsubstantial death is amorous,
		And that the lean abhorred monster keeps
		Thee here in dark to be his paramour?
		For fear of that, I still will stay with thee,
20		And never from this palace of dim night
		Depart again. Here, here will I remain
		With worms that are thy chamber-maids. O here
		Will I set up my everlasting rest;
		And shake the yoke of inauspicious stars
25		From this world-wearied flesh. Eyes, look your last.
		Arms, take your last embrace. And lips, O you
		The doors of breath, seal with a righteous kiss
		A dateless bargain to engrossing death.
		[*Takes out the poison*] Come bitter conduct, come unsavoury
30		guide,
		Thou desperate pilot, now at once run on
		The dashing rocks thy sea-sick weary bark.
		Here's to my love! [*Drinks*] O true apothecary!
		Thy drugs are quick. Thus with a kiss I die.

Marks

(*a*) Describe **briefly** the circumstances at this moment in the play which explain Romeo's preoccupation with death.   **1**

(*b*) Explain how the punctuation of lines 1–4 helps to show Romeo's feelings.   **2**

(*c*) Comment on the effectiveness of the image in lines 7–9.   **2**

(*d*) (i) Show, by referring to lines 14–22, how dramatic irony heightens the tension at this moment.   **4**

   (ii) By referring to another scene in the play, show how dramatic irony increases the audience's involvement.   **4**

(*e*) "Eyes, look your last.
   ... A dateless bargain to engrossing death." (lines 25–28)

   Assess the contribution of **two** of the following in making these lines effective:

   (i) rhythm;

   (ii) sound;

   (iii) sentence structure;

   (iv) imagery.   **4**

(*f*) Romeo is often said to be too impulsive and emotional. Would you agree with this? In support of your answer you should refer briefly to this extract, and in more detail to one other scene.   **8**

   (25)

1996

You are reminded of the instruction on the front cover about the use of texts.

2.   ROBERT BURNS

Read the song carefully and answer the questions which follow. The number of marks attached to each question will give a clear indication of the length of answer required.

AE FOND KISS

Ae fond kiss, and then we sever—
Ae fareweel, and then—for ever
Deep in heart-wrung tears I'll pledge thee!
Warring sighs and groans I'll wage thee!

5   Who shall say that fortune grieves him,
While the star of hope she leaves him?
Me, nae chearfu' twinkle lights me—
Dark despair around benights me.

I'll ne'er blame my partial fancy,
10   Naething could resist my Nancy;
But to see her, was to love her—
Love but her, and love for ever.

Had we never lov'd sae kindly—
Had we never lov'd sae blindly—
15   Never met—or never parted,
We had ne'er been broken-hearted!

Fare-thee-weel, thou first and fairest!
Fare-thee-weel, thou best and dearest!
Thine be ilka joy and treasure,
20   Peace, Enjoyment, Love, and Pleasure!

Ae fond kiss, and then we sever!
Ae fareweel, alas! for ever!
Deep in heart-wrung tears I'll pledge thee
Warring sighs and groans I'll wage thee.

Marks

(a)   (i) What do we learn about the poet's situation from stanza 1?   **1**

  (ii) Select one image from stanza 1 and show how it helps to convey the intensity of the poet's feelings.   **2**

(b)   Trace the changes in mood that occur from stanza 2 to the end of the poem, supporting your comments with close reference to the language of the poem.   **4**

(c)   Burns often uses simple, everyday language as well as a more formal artificial style.
  (i) Identify one example of each from this poem.   **1**
  (ii) Which style do you find more effective in expressing the poet's feelings? Justify your choice.   **3**

(d)   Show to what extent your appreciation of the poem depends on any **two** of the following:
  (i) sound;
  (ii) rhythm;
  (iii) rhyme;
  (iv) structural features.   **4**

(e)   As fully as you can, compare and contrast "Ae Fond Kiss" with any other love song written by Burns.   **10**

(25)

52

You are reminded of the instruction on the front cover about the use of texts.

3.   *NORTH AND SOUTH*

Read the extract carefully and answer the questions which follow. The number of marks attached to each question will give a clear indication of the length of answer required.

The extract is taken from the chapter entitled "Comfort in Sorrow" which is concerned mainly with events in Nicholas Higgins's life.

So they questioned and listened. The workmen's calculations were based (like too many of the masters') on false premises. They reckoned on their fellow-men as if they possessed the calculable powers of machines, no more, no less; no allowance for human passions getting the better of reason, as in the case of Boucher and the rioters; and believing that the representations of their injuries would have the same
5   effect on strangers far away, as the injuries (fancied or real) had upon themselves. They were consequently surprised and indignant at the poor Irish, who had allowed themselves to be imported and brought over to take their places. This indignation was tempered, in some degree, by contempt for "them Irishers", and by pleasure at the idea of the bungling way in which they would set to work, and perplex their new masters with their ignorance and stupidity, strange exaggerated stories of which were
10   already spreading through the town. But the most cruel cut of all was that of the Milton workmen, who had defied and disobeyed the commands of the Union to keep the peace, whatever came; who had originated discord in the camp, and spread the panic of the law being arrayed against them.

"And so the strike is at an end," said Margaret.

"Ay, miss. It's save as save can. Th' factory doors will need open wide to-morrow to let in all who'll be
15   axing for work; if it's only just to show they'd nought to do wi' a measure, which if we'd been made o' th' right stuff would ha' brought wages up to a point they'n not been at this ten year."

"You'll get work, shan't you?" asked Margaret. "You're a famous workman, are not you?"

"Hamper 'll let me work at his mill, when he cuts off his right hand—not before, and not at after," said Nicholas quietly. Margaret was silenced and sad.

20   "About the wages," said Mr Hale. "You'll not be offended, but I think you make some sad mistakes. I should like to read you some remarks in a book I have." He got up and went to his book-shelves.

"Yo' needn't trouble yoursel', sir," said Nicholas. "Their book-stuff goes in at one ear and out at t'other. I can make nought on't. Afore Hamper and me had this split, th' overlooker telled him I were stirring up th' men to ask for higher wages; and Hamper met me one day in th' yard. He'd a thin book i'
25   his hand, and says he, 'Higgins, I'm told you're one of those damned fools that think you can get higher wages for asking for 'em; ay, and keep 'em up too, when you've forced 'em up. Now, I'll give yo' a chance and try if yo've any sense in yo'. Here's a book written by a friend o' mine, and if yo'll read it yo'll see how wages find their own level, without either masters or men having aught to do with them; except the men cut their own throats wi' striking, like the confounded noodles they are.' Well, now, sir,
30   I put it to yo', being a parson, and having been in th' preaching line, and having had to try and bring folk o'er to what yo' thought was a right way o' thinking—did yo' begin by calling 'em fools and such like, or didn't yo' rather give 'em such kind words at first, to make 'em ready for to listen and be convinced, if they could; and in yo'r preaching, did yo' stop every now and then, and say, half to them and half to yo'rsel, 'But yo're such a pack o' fools, that I've a strong notion it's no use my trying to put
35   sense into yo'?' I were not i' th' best state, I'll own, for taking in what Hamper's friend had to say—I were so vexed at the way it were put to me;—but I thought, 'Come, I'll see what these chaps has got to say, and try if it's them or me as is th' noodle.' So I took th' book and tugged at it; but, Lord bless yo', it went on about capital and labour, and labour and capital, till it fair sent me off to sleep. I ne'er could rightly fix i' my mind which was which; and it spoke on 'em as if they was vartues or vices; and what I
40   wanted for to know were the rights o' men, whether they were rich or poor—so be they only were men."

Marks

(*a*) What is the connection between Margaret and Nicholas Higgins, and what two major events have just occurred in his life?

4

(*b*) Which two false premises, according to the narrator, had the strike been built upon? Answer in your own words.

2

(*c*) By close reference to the language of lines 5–10, show how different attitudes towards the Irish workers emerge.

4

(*d*) (i) Nicholas's speech is written in a representation of the Lancashire dialect of the area of Milton. From lines 22 to 24, identify an example of vocabulary and an example of grammar which seem typical of this dialect and show how each differs from standard English.

2

 (ii) What advantages and/or disadvantages do you perceive in using such dialect throughout the novel?

3

(*e*) Industrial relations play an important part in the novel. Show how Mr Thornton's attitude to industrial relations changes in the course of the novel. Identify who and/or what events cause these alterations in his views, and indicate how convincing you find these changes.

10

(25)

You are reminded of the instruction on the front cover about the use of texts.

4. *THE DEVIL'S DISCIPLE*

Read the extract carefully and answer the questions which follow. The number of marks attached to each question will give a clear indication of the length of answer required.

This extract is from the last scene in the play.

ANDERSON:	[*exhaling a deep breath of relief, and dabbing his perspiring brow with his handkerchief*] Thank God, I was in time!
BURGOYNE:	[*calm as ever, and still watch in hand*] Ample time, sir. Plenty of time. I should never dream of hanging any gentleman by an American clock. [*He puts up his watch.*]
5 ANDERSON:	Yes: we are some minutes ahead of you already, General. Now tell them to take the rope from the neck of that American citizen.
BURGOYNE:	[*to the executioner in the cart—very politely*] Kindly undo Mr Dudgeon.
	The executioner takes the rope from Richard's neck, unties his hands, and helps him on with his coat.
10 JUDITH:	[*stealing timidly to Anderson*] Tony.
ANDERSON:	[*putting his arm round her shoulders and bantering her affectionately*] Well, what do you think of your husband now, eh?—eh??—eh???
JUDITH:	I am ashamed—[*She hides her face against his breast.*]
BURGOYNE:	[*to Swindon*] You look disappointed, Major Swindon.
15 SWINDON:	You look defeated, General Burgoyne.
BURGOYNE:	I am, sir; and I am humane enough to be glad of it. [*Richard jumps down from the cart, Brudenell offering his hand to help him, and runs to Anderson, whose left hand he shakes heartily, the right being occupied by Judith.*] By the way, Mr Anderson, I do not quite understand. The safe-conduct was for a commander of the militia. I understand you are a—[*He looks as pointedly as his good manners permit at the riding boots, the pistols, and Richard's coat, and adds*]—a clergyman.
ANDERSON:	[*between Judith and Richard*] Sir: it is in the hour of trial that a man finds his true profession. This foolish young man [*placing his hand on Richard's shoulder*] boasted himself the Devil's Disciple; but when the hour of trial came to him, he found that it was his destiny to suffer and be faithful to the death. I thought myself a decent minister of the gospel of peace; but when the hour of trial came to me, I found that it was my destiny to be a man of action, and that my place was amid the thunder of the captains and the shouting. So I am starting life at fifty as Captain Anthony Anderson of the Springtown militia; and the Devil's Disciple here will start presently as the Reverend Richard Dudgeon, and wag his pow in my old pulpit, and give good advice to this silly sentimental little wife of mine [*putting his other hand on her shoulder. She steals a glance at Richard to see how the prospect pleases him.*]. Your mother told me, Richard, that I should never have chosen Judith if I'd been born for the ministry. I am afraid she was right; so, by your leave, you may keep my coat and I'll keep yours.
35 RICHARD:	Minister—I should say Captain. I have behaved like a fool.
JUDITH:	Like a hero.
RICHARD:	Much the same thing, perhaps.

Marks

(*a*) Briefly describe what Anthony Anderson has done since he left Websterbridge the day before. **1**

(*b*) Both Burgoyne and Anderson use the idea of time in lines 1–5 to score points off each other. Explain how each of them does this. **4**

(*c*) Using your knowledge of the three characters, give an explanation of the emotion ascribed to each of them in lines 13–15. **3**

(*d*) (i) What is the relationship in the play between Burgoyne and Swindon? **1**

  (ii) How is the language of lines 14–16 structured to convey their relationship at this point in the play? **2**

(*e*) How appropriate to its subject matter do you find the language of Anderson's speech (lines 22–31)? (You may find it helpful to refer to such features as sentence structure, punctuation, word choice, imagery . . .) **4**

(*f*) The fool or the hero? Explain which of these terms seems to you to be the more accurate in describing Richard's role throughout the play. **10**

(25)

You are reminded of the instruction on the front cover about the use of texts.

5. *THE INHERITORS*

Read the extract carefully and answer the questions which follow. The number of marks attached to each question will give a clear indication of the length of answer required.

Fa has been swept to her death, over the fall, and only Lok remains.

The creature stood and the splashes of moonlight stirred over it. The eye-hollows gazed not at the bone but at an invisible point towards the river. Now the right leg began to move. The creature's attention seemed to gather and focus in the leg and the foot began to pick and search in the earth like a hand. The big toe bored and gripped and the toes folded round an object that had been almost completely buried in
5 the churned soil. The foot rose, the leg bent and presented an object to the lowered hand. The head came down a little, the gaze swept inward from that invisible point and regarded what was in the hand. It was a root, old and rotted, worn away at both ends but preserving the exaggerated contours of a female body.

The creature looked again towards the water. Both hands were full, the bar of its brow glistened in the
10 moonlight, over the great caverns where the eyes were hidden. There was light poured down over the cheek-bones and the wide lips and there was a twist of light caught like a white hair in every curl. But the caverns were dark as though already the whole head was nothing but a skull.

The water rat concluded from the creature's stillness that it was not dangerous. It came with a quick rush from under the bush and began to cross the open space, it forgot the silent figure and searched
15 busily for something to eat.

There was light now in each cavern, lights faint as the starlight reflected in the crystals of a granite cliff. The lights increased, acquired definition, brightened, lay each sparkling at the lower edge of a cavern. Suddenly, noiselessly, the lights became thin crescents, went out, and streaks glistened on each cheek. The lights appeared again, caught among the silvered curls of the beard. They hung, elongated,
20 dropped from curl to curl and gathered at the lowest tip. The streaks on the cheeks pulsed as the drops swam down them, a great drop swelled at the end of a hair of the beard, shivering and bright. It detached itself and fell in a silver flash, striking a withered leaf with a sharp pat. The water rat scurried away and plopped into the river.

Stealthily the moonlight moved the blue shadows. The creature pulled its right foot out of the mire and
25 took a lurching step forward. It staggered in a half-circle until it reached the gap between the thorn bushes where the broad track began. It started to run along the track and it was blue and grey in the moonlight. It went laboriously, slowly, with much bobbing up and down of the head. It limped. When it reached the slope up to the top of the fall it was on all fours.

On the terrace the creature moved faster. It ran to the far end where the water was coming down from
30 the ice in a cascade. It turned, came back, and crept on all fours into the hollow where the other figure was. The creature wrestled with a rock that was lying on a mound of earth but was too weak to move it. At last it gave up and crawled round the hollow by the remains of a fire. It came close to the ashes and lay on its side. It pulled its legs up, knees against the chest. It folded its hands under its cheek and lay still. The twisted and smoothed root lay before its face. It made no noise, but seemed to be growing
35 into the earth, drawing the soft flesh of its body into a contact so close that the movements of pulse and breathing were inhibited.

Marks

(*a*)   (i)   Why is the creature gazing "at an invisible point towards the river" (line 2)?   1

       (ii)   What takes up his attention in the rest of the first paragraph?   2

(*b*)   Read again the third, fourth and fifth paragraphs (lines 13–28). By referring closely to all three paragraphs, show how Golding in different ways creates sympathy for "the creature".   6

(*c*)   One notable feature of Golding's style is the way he provides echoes of things that happened earlier in the story. By commenting on at least two such "echoes", show this to be the case in this extract.   6

(*d*)   In the earlier chapters, Golding had presented us with "the people" and their experiences; Lok is now described, in this extract, as "the creature"; and in the final chapter (which follows this extract) Golding places us exclusively with "the new people".

     Explain how this structuring helps to illuminate some of the themes and concerns of the novel.   **10**

                                                                (25)

You are reminded of the instruction on the front cover about the use of texts.

6.   IAIN CRICHTON SMITH

Read the poem carefully and answer the questions which follow. The number of marks attached to each question will give a clear indication of the length of answer required.

AT THE SALE

Old beds, old chairs, old mattresses, old books,
old pictures of coiffed women, hatted men,
ministers with clamped lips and flowing beards,
a Duke in his Highland den,
5   and, scattered among these, old copper fire-guards,
stone water-bottles, stoves and shepherds' crooks.

How much goes out of fashion and how soon!
The double-columned leather-covered tomes
recall those praying Covenanters still
10   adamant against Rome's
adamant empire. Every article
is soaked in time and dust and sweat and rust. What tune

warbled from that phonograph? Who played
that gap-toothed dumb piano? Who once moved
15   with that white chamber pot through an ancient room?
And who was it that loved
to see her own reflection in the gloom
of that webbed mirror? And who was it that prayed

holding that Bible in her fading hands?
20   The auctioneer's quick eyes swoop on a glance,
a half-seen movement. In the inner ring
a boy in serious stance
holds up a fan, a piece of curtaining,
an hour-glass with its trickle of old sand.

25   We walk around and find an old machine.
On one side pump, on another turn a wheel.
But nothing happens. What's this object for?
Imagine how we will
endlessly pump and turn for forty years
30   and then receive a pension, smart and clean,

climbing a dais to such loud applause
as shakes the hall for toiling without fail
at this strange nameless gadget, pumping, turning,
each day oiling the wheel
35   with zeal and eagerness and freshness burning
in a happy country of anonymous laws,

while the ghostly hands are clapping and the chairs
grow older as we look, the pictures fade,
the stone is changed to rubber, and the wheel
40   elaborates its rayed
brilliance and complexity and we feel
the spade become a scoop, cropping the grass,

and the flesh itself becomes unnecessary.
O hold me, love, in this appalling place.
45   Let your hand stay me by this mattress here
and this tall ruined glass,
by this dismembered radio, this queer
machine that waits and has no history.

Marks

(a)   (i)   How does the choice of items mentioned in stanza 1 establish the theme of the poem?   2

    (ii)   Show how stanza 2 develops the theme established in stanza 1.   2

(b)   (i)   In stanza 1 the poet listed a series of domestic items; in stanza 3 he offers a series of questions. Explain in what way(s) his focus of attention has changed in stanza 3.   2

    (ii)   What is the cumulative effect of the five questions asked in lines 12–19?   2

(c)   Re-read lines 25–43 ("We walk around . . . flesh itself becomes unnecessary.").

Examine the line of thought in this section. By close reference to these lines, show how the "machine" of line 25 is central to the poet's line of thought.   4

(d)   Examine carefully the last five lines of the poem.

To what extent do you find this a satisfactory conclusion in relation to the themes and ideas of the poem as a whole?   5

(e)   By referring in detail to one other poem by Crichton Smith, show how

    (i)   he relates people to their place in time, and

    (ii)   he underlines the significance of the passing of time.   8

(25)

You are reminded of the instruction on the front cover about the use of texts.

7. *BOLD GIRLS*

Read the extract carefully and answer the questions which follow. The number of marks attached to each question will give a clear indication of the length of answer required.

In the following extract, Nora, Cassie and Marie have returned from a night out.

NORA [*pleading*]: Cassie . . .

CASSIE: Good-night, Mummy. [*She looks away from Nora*]

NORA [*drawing herself up*]: Oh you'll be telling me a different tale in the morning! There's no end to your wild tales, Cassie! There's no end to them, Marie! [*She snatches up her drink and takes an angry gulp*]

5   And I'd it all to do. I'd it all to put up with! Are you hearing me?

Cassie doesn't look at Nora.

[*Taking another gulp*] He's lost my remnant, Marie. He's lost it. I'd all the money saved, as good as paid. It's gone he says, gone. I'll never find a colour like that again. Months I'd been dreaming of the glow that would give my front room. Months. And he's lost it. I'll never have it the way I want

10   it now. Never. [*She is getting tearful in her turn*] My lovely wee room. It could be lovely, couldn't it, Marie?

MARIE: You'll get it right, Nora.

NORA: Well where will I ever find a colour like that again? Tell me that? [*Waiting for a response*] Cassie? I'm asking you!

15   CASSIE [*looking up at Nora*]: Good night, Mummy.

Nora stares at her for a moment, then she nods.

NORA: Well I'm going up the town tomorrow. I'm just going to go up the town and buy a piece of what I want. I'll get credit. I'll give them a false address and I'll get credit and I'll have my loose covers. And if you don't want to come and help choose them, Cassie, you needn't sit on them.

20   *Nora exits.*

Marie puts the gin bottle down in front of Cassie. Cassie helps herself to another drink.

MARIE [*quietly*]: It'll tear the heart out of her, Cassie.

CASSIE: Mummy's heart is made of steel. She had to grow it that way.

Marie reaches over and takes Michael's picture. She goes and rehangs it carefully.

25   There's a waitress up that club will be walking round without her hair tomorrow if I can find her.

MARIE: You don't know it was her. There's people in and out of here all the time.

CASSIE: Who else would it be?

MARIE: Well—if she's thieving round the club there'll be others sort her out before you do. [*She steps back to admire the picture*]

30   CASSIE: How do you stand it here, Marie?

MARIE: Sure where else would I go?

CASSIE: How do you keep that smile on your face?

MARIE: Super-glue.

CASSIE: There's not one piece of bitterness in you, is there?

35   MARIE: Oh Cassie.

CASSIE: You see, you're good. And I'm just wicked.

MARIE: Aye you're a bold woman altogether.

CASSIE: Is it hard being good?

MARIE: I took lessons.

40   CASSIE: Well, tell me what you've got to smile about, Marie, because I'm sure I can't see it.

MARIE: I've a lot to be thankful of. I've my kids, a job, a nice wee house and I can still pay for it.

CASSIE: You've two wee boys growing out of their clothes faster than you can get them new ones, a part-time job licking envelopes for a wage that wouldn't keep a budgie and three red bills on your mantelpiece there.

45   MARIE: That's what's great about a Saturday out with you, Cassie, you just know how to look at the bright side of things, don't you? '

CASSIE: Well just tell me how you can keep filling that kettle and making folk tea without pouring it over their head?

MARIE: Ah well you see, I'm a mug.

50 CASSIE: I think you are.

MARIE: I didn't marry Joe, but . . .

CASSIE: No. You did not. That mug was me.

MARIE: See, Cassie, I've had better times with Michael than a lot of women get in their whole lives with a man.

55 CASSIE: And that keeps you going?

MARIE: It's a warming kind of thought.

Marks

(a) Explain briefly the reason for Nora's pleading with Cassie (line 1). 1

(b) (i) By referring closely to lines 3–19, describe the changes in Nora's mood. 3

(ii) To what extent are these changes in mood typical of Nora's character in the play as a whole? Refer to other parts of the play in your answer. 5

(c) Comment on the significance at this point in the play of the stage directions about Michael's picture (line 24 and lines 28–29). 2

(d) By referring closely to the language and pace of the dialogue between Marie and Cassie (lines 22–56), show what aspects of each character are revealed. 6

(e) To what extent would you agree that *Bold Girls* presents us with a picture of women's lives which is of universal significance? You should refer closely to more than one part of the play in your answer. 8

(25)

You are reminded of the instruction on the front cover about the use of texts.

8.   *SUNSET SONG*

Read the extract carefully and answer the questions which follow. The number of marks attached to each question will give a clear indication of the length of answer required.

Winter has descended on Blawearie.

None of them spoke for long, listening to that whoom and blatter on the window-panes, and the clap-clap-clap of some loose slate far up on the roof, till father whispered and looked at them, his whisper hurt worse than a shout, *God, I wonder why Jean left us?*

5   Chris cried then, making no sound, she looked at Will and saw him with his face red and shamed, all three of them thinking of mother, her that was by them so kind and friendly and quick that last New Year, so cold and quiet and forgotten now with the little dead twins in the kirkyard of Kinraddie, piling black with the driving of the snow it would be under the rustle and swing and creak of the yews. And Will stared at father, his face was blind with pity, once he made to speak, but couldn't, always they'd hated one the other so much and they'd feel shamed if they spoke in friendship now.

10   So father took up his paper again and at ten o'clock Chris went out to milk the kye and Will went with her over the close, carrying the lantern, the flame of it leapt and starred and quivered and hesitated in the drive of the snow. In the light of it, like a rain of arrows they saw the coming of the storm that night swept down from the Grampian heuchs, thick and strong it was in Blawearie, but high in the real hills a smoring, straight wall must be sweeping the dark, blinding down against the lone huts of the shepherds

15   and the faces of lost tinks tramping through it looking for lights the snow'd smothered long before. Chris was shaking, but not with cold, and inside the byre she leant on a stall and Will said *God, you look awful, what is 't?* And she shook herself and said *Nothing. Why haven't you gone to see Mollie to-night?*

He said he was going next day, wasn't that enough, he'd be a corpse long ere he reached Drumlithie to-night—*listen to the wind, it'll blow the damn place down on our lugs in a minute!* And the byre shook,

20   between the lulls it seemed to set its breath to rise and take from the hill-side into the air, there was such straining and creaking. Not that the calves or the stirks paid heed, they slept and snored in their stalls with never a care, there were worse things in the world than being a beast.

Back in the house it seemed to Chris she'd but hardly sieved the milk when the great clock ben in the parlour sent peal after peal out dirling through the place. Will looked at Chris and the two at father, and

25   John Guthrie was just raising up his head from his paper, but if he'd been to wish them a happy New Year or not they were never to know, for right at that minute there came a brisk chap at the door and somebody lifted the sneck and stamped the snow from his feet and banged the door behind him.

And there he was, Long Rob of the Mill, muffled in a great grey cravat and with leggings up to the knees, covered and frosted from head to foot in the snow, he cried *Happy New Year to you all! Am I the*

30   *first?* And John Guthrie was up on his feet, *Ay, man, you're fairly that, out of that coat of yours!* They stripped off the coat between them, faith! Rob's mouser was nearly frozen, but he said it was fine and laughed, and waited the glass of toddy father brought him and cried *Your health!* And just as it went down his throat there came a new knock, damn't if it wasn't Chae Strachan, he'd had more than a drink already and he cried *Happy New Year, I'm the first foot in am I not?* And he made to kiss Chris, she

35   wouldn't have minded, laughing, but he slithered and couped on the floor, Long Rob peered down at him and cried out, shocked-like, *God Almighty, Chae, you can't sleep there!*

So he was hoisted into a chair and was better in a minute when he'd had another drink.

Marks

(a) To what extent do you consider John Guthrie's mood, as demonstrated in lines 1–3, to be typical of his character in the novel as a whole? Justify your answer. **3**

(b) By referring to lines 4–9, explain the reactions of Chris and Will to their father's whispered words. **4**

(c) (i) By referring closely to lines 1–22, assess the contribution made by the weather to the scene. In your answer you may wish to refer to: sound; imagery; contrast. **6**

    (ii) From the arrival of Long Rob onwards, the mood of the scene changes. Show how this is achieved by referring to **two** of the following: dialogue; action; the language of the narrator. **4**

(d) To what extent would you agree that *Sunset Song*'s strength lies in its depiction of the relationship between people and place? You should refer in your answer briefly to the passage and in more detail to **one** other part of the novel. **8**

(25)

You are reminded of the instruction on the front cover about the use of texts.

9.   PHILIP LARKIN

Read the poem carefully and answer the questions which follow. The number of marks attached to each question will give a clear indication of the length of answer required.

AN ARUNDEL TOMB

Side by side, their faces blurred,
The earl and countess lie in stone,
Their proper habits vaguely shown
As jointed armour, stiffened pleat,
5   And that faint hint of the absurd—
The little dogs under their feet.

Such plainness of the pre-baroque
Hardly involves the eye, until
It meets his left-hand gauntlet, still
10   Clasped empty in the other; and
One sees, with a sharp tender shock,
His hand withdrawn, holding her hand.

They would not think to lie so long.
Such faithfulness in effigy
15   Was just a detail friends would see:
A sculptor's sweet commissioned grace
Thrown off in helping to prolong
The Latin names around the base.

They would not guess how early in
20   Their supine stationary voyage
The air would change to soundless damage,
Turn the old tenantry away;
How soon succeeding eyes begin
To look, not read. Rigidly they

25   Persisted, linked, through lengths and breadths
Of time. Snow fell, undated. Light
Each summer thronged the glass. A bright
Litter of birdcalls strewed the same
Bone-riddled ground. And up the paths
30   The endless altered people came,

Washing at their identity.
Now, helpless in the hollow of
An unarmorial age, a trough
Of smoke in slow suspended skeins
35   Above their scrap of history,
Only an attitude remains:

Time has transfigured them into
Untruth. The stone fidelity
They hardly meant has come to be
40   Their final blazon, and to prove
Our almost-instinct almost true:
What will survive of us is love.

Marks

(a) What detail of the tomb comes as a surprise to the poet in stanza 2? By referring closely to the language, show how that surprise is conveyed to the reader.

2

(b) What is implied about the sculptor's attitude to his task in lines 16–18, and which word(s) especially help(s) to make the implication(s) clear?

2

(c) By referring closely to the poetic techniques used in lines 19–29, show how the age of the tomb is emphasised.

4

(d)   "And up the paths
The endless altered people came,
Washing at their identity."

Comment on the effectiveness of these lines in showing how attitudes to the couple have changed over the years.

3

(e) Identify the heraldic imagery used in the last two stanzas and comment on its appropriateness in this poem.

3

(f) How is the "untruth" mentioned in line 38 developed in the last stanza?

3

(g) Choose another poem in which Larkin deals with the effects of time. Compare his use of time in the poem you have chosen with his use of time in *An Arundel Tomb*.

8

(25)

PART 2—CRITICAL ESSAY

Attempt ONE question only, taken from any of the Sections A to D.

In all Sections you may use Scottish texts.

You should spend about 50 minutes on this part of the paper.

Begin your answer on a fresh page.

If you use a Specified Text as the basis for your Critical Essay, you must not rely ONLY on any extract printed in Part 1 in this paper. If you attempt Section C—Poetry, you should note the additional instruction at the head of Section C.

SECTION A—DRAMA

> **If you have answered on a play in the Specified Text option in Part 1 of the paper, you must not attempt a question from this Drama Section.**
>
> **In your answer in this Section you should, where relevant, refer to such features as dialogue, characterisation, plot, theme, scene, climax, style, structure.**

1. "At the end of most of his plays, order is restored, evil is defeated and good re-established."

   In any play by Shakespeare, examine how he establishes or reveals a threat to the natural order of things. To what extent does he then ensure that that threat is defeated or removed by the end of the play?

2. "Drama is often a window on a limited area of individual experience—and yet major themes of significance to us all are explored."

   Choose a play which deals with individual experience and show how it explores both individual experience and themes of universal significance.

3. What characters actually do; what characters say; what other characters say about them—there are many ways by which a playwright can create a character.

   From a play or plays which you have studied, examine the techniques the author has used to make a character or characters convincing.

4. Often the performance of a play on stage differs significantly from the impressions left by the reading of the same play. If you have both read and seen a production of a play, show how the production altered your perceptions of an incident, or a character, or a theme.

SECTION B—PROSE

> **If you have answered on a prose work in the Specified Text option in Part 1 of the paper, you must not attempt a question from this Prose Section.**
>
> **In your answer in this Section you should, where relevant, refer to such features as setting, theme, characterisation, plot, content, style, structure, language, narrative stance, symbolism.**

5. By referring in detail to any prose work which you have read, show how its setting **in time** contributes to the themes and ideas of the work.

6. Authors are often characterised as being "Crime writers", or "Romance writers", or "Historical novelists", or known by some other such stereotyping label. Show how such a writer also explores themes and/or characters which are of interest to a much wider readership.

7. Isolation, rejection, confrontation, or loneliness are major themes that are explored in many novels and short stories.

   By examining the techniques used by an author, show how one of these themes is dealt with in a way which you found meaningful in one or more texts.

8. Choose a form of written argument or discourse (eg an essay or a piece of journalism) which successfully presents an argument or a point of view. By close reference to the text, show how the author makes his/her argument convincing to you.

9. With reference to a novel or short story of your choice, show how the writer has created a believable world.

SECTION C—POETRY

> **If you have answered on a poem in the Specified Text option in Part 1 of the paper, you must not attempt a question from this Poetry Section. You may not base an answer on Burns's "Ae Fond Kiss", Crichton Smith's "At The Sale" or on Larkin's "An Arundel Tomb".**
>
> **In your answer in this Section you should, where relevant, refer to such features as rhyme, rhythm, word-choice, language, sound, imagery, symbolism, style, structure.**

10. Some poets succeed in presenting fresh and unusual insights by using everyday speech patterns and vocabulary. Their work may, for example, include the use of cliché, or informal expressions or idioms.

    Examine the work of a poet who may be described in this way and explain how he/she succeeds in providing the reader with new insights. (You may deal with more than one poem in your answer.)

11. Many memorable poems leave the reader with a powerful impression of a person, a place, or an era.

    Using a poem which has left you with such an impression, explain what techniques are used by the poet to convey this impression.

12. If you have read the work of a poet who, in your view, has a recognisable "voice", describe what contributes to his/her particular individuality, or personality, as a poet, and explain what features of his/her work you enjoy. You should refer in some detail to more than one poem.

13. The form of a poem can add significantly to its impact. Choose a poem whose form clearly contributes to its impact. Explain in some detail how the form of the poem supports and/or amplifies the overall effect of the poem.

SECTION D—MASS MEDIA

If your Review of Personal Reading is based entirely on a radio, television or film script, you must not attempt a question from this Mass Media Section.

14. From a film, choose a sequence which you consider to be well made and of key importance. By closely referring to mise-en-scène, montage and soundtrack, explain your view of the sequence and its importance to the film as a whole.

15. Choose a star who brings a particular image to his/her films. Briefly explain how the star's image was constructed, and show how it affected your response to his/her films. (You should refer to more than one film in your answer.)

16. To what extent would you agree that in public life, success depends on image and presentation rather than on the reality of person and policy? You should refer closely in your answer to texts in more than one medium.

17. Choose a text which represents a group in society in a way which affected your views. By closely referring to the text, explain how these representations were constructed and why they changed your views.

18. By close reference to one, or more than one, sequence in a television play, series or serial you have enjoyed, show how the programme-makers exploited the medium in order to enhance your pleasure in the drama. (You may refer to such features as use of camera, soundtrack, structure . . .)

19. Choose a television play, series or serial which successfully explores the subject of family in contemporary society. By referring to key sequences, show what messages are given about the family and explain why you consider the drama to be successful.

[END OF QUESTION PAPER]

SCOTTISH
CERTIFICATE OF
EDUCATION
1997

TUESDAY, 6 MAY
9.15 AM – 11.20 AM

ENGLISH
HIGHER GRADE
Paper I

There are **two parts** to this paper, Part 1 (Interpretation) and Part 2 (Report). You should attempt both parts.

Part 1 (Interpretation), on pages 2, 3 and 4, is worth 40 marks. There is one passage, with questions following. Use the left-hand margin of the answer book to indicate clearly the questions attempted.

Part 2 (Report), on pages 6, 7 and 8, is worth 35 marks. You should begin your Report on a fresh page of the answer book.

PART 1—INTERPRETATION

You should spend approximately 1 hour on this part of the paper, including reading time. There is ONE passage and questions.

Read the passage carefully and then answer all the questions which follow on page four. **Use your own words whenever possible and particularly when you are instructed to do so.** The number of marks attached to each question will give some indication of the kind of answer required.

In the passage below, William McIlvanney, author of the novel "Docherty", remembers his upbringing and considers its significance in his development as a writer.

I remember as a boy being alone in the living-room of our council-house in Kilmarnock. I would be maybe 11 years old. I was lying in front of the coal fire with my head resting on an armchair. It was, I think, late on a winter afternoon. The window had gone black and I hadn't put the light on, enjoying the small cave of brightness and heat the fire had hewn from the dark. Perhaps I was a far traveller resting by his camp-fire.
5   Perhaps I was a knight keeping vigil for the dawn when wondrous deeds would be done. For I could be many people at that time as I still can.

I don't know how I came to be alone at that time in that place. In our house with six not unnoticeable presences, it wasn't an easy trick to be alone, even without counting the cavalcade of aunties and uncles and cousins and friends who seemed to be constantly passing through. I wonder if I had come home from school to find the
10   house empty. But that seems improbable. My mother was a ferocious carer who had an almost mystical capacity to conjure solid worries out of air that to the rest of us looked untroubled and clear. Maybe somebody else was supposed to be with me and had gone out briefly.

I don't know. I am simply aware of myself there. The moment sits separate and vivid in my memory, without explanation, like a rootless flower. Whoever I was being, traveller or knight, I must have been tired. For I fell
15   asleep.

The awakening was strange. I think I must have been aware of the noise of people entering the house, one of those slow fuses of sound that sputteringly traverses the unconscious until it ignites into waking. My consciousness and the room came into the light together. My eyes were bruised with brightness. What I saw seems in retrospect to have had the shiningness of newly minted coins, all stamped unmistakably as genuine,
20   pure metal, the undepreciable currency of my life.

What I saw in fact was pretty banal. My father had his hand on the light-switch he had just pressed. My mother was beside him. They were both laughing at what must have been my startled eyes and my wonderment at being where I was. Around them was a room made instantly out of the dark. It was a very ordinary room. But it was wonderful. How strange the biscuit barrel was where my mother kept the rent-money. How unimaginable was

25   the image of Robert Burns with the mouse, painted on glass by my uncle. How incorrigibly itself the battered sideboard became. The room was full of amazing objects. They might as well have come from Pompeii.

And at the centre of them were two marvellously familiar strangers. I saw them not just as my mother and father. I knew suddenly how dark my father was, how physical his presence. His laughter filled the room, coming from a place that was his alone. My mother looked strangely young, coming in fresh-faced from the cold and
30   darkness, her irises swallowing her pupils as she laughed in the shocking brightness. I felt an inordinate love for them. I experienced the transformation of the ordinary into something powerfully mysterious.

I'm convinced that that moment in the living-room at St Maurs Crescent is one of the experiences from which *Docherty* (and perhaps everything I've written) grew. It was a moment which has had many relatives. When I consider them, I realise that they have several features in common.

35   One of them is a belief in the grandeur of the everyday, where the ordinary is just the unique in hiding. As it says in *Docherty*, "messiahs are born in stables". That being so, as a boy I kept finding Bethlehem round every corner. So many things amazed me.

There were the stories surrounding me, for a start. *Docherty*, I should think, began its gestation in the mouths of the people all around me. Our house was an incredible talking-shop. As the youngest of four, I seem to have
40   grown up with an intense conversation going on endlessly about me as my natural habitat. By one of those casually important accidents of childhood, the youngest of us had to sleep in a fold-down bed in the living-room. Lack of space had its advantages. This meant that from a very early age, I could be involved, however marginally, in these debates, often going to sleep with the sound of disputation as a lullaby.

To this continuing seminar on life and the strange nature of it came many visiting speakers. Our house often felt
45   to me like a throughway for talk. Relatives and friends were always dropping in. They brought news of local doings, bizarre attitudes, memorable remarks made under pressure, anecdotes of wild behaviour. Most of it was delivered and received with a calmness that astonished me. I vaguely sensed, early on, the richness they were casually living among, rather as if a traveller should come upon the Incas using pure gold as kitchen utensils. The substance that would be *Docherty* was beginning to glint for me in fragments of talk and caught
50   glimpses of living.

Cognate to my awareness of the rich and largely uncommemorated life around me was a fascination with language. Given my background, I was lucky to be in a house where books were part of the practical furniture, not there as ornaments but to be read and talked about. My mother was the source of the activity. My sister and my two brothers had established reading as a family tradition by the time I was old enough to join in. Only my
55   father, someone—it has always seemed to me—educated spectacularly below his abilities, was never to be comfortable with books. His presence on the edges of our immersion in reading became, I think, in some way formative for me. I wanted him somehow to be included in the words.

Love of reading led naturally, it seemed at the time, to efforts at writing. If books were not the most sought-after domestic adjuncts in our housing scheme (depraved orgies of poetry-reading behind closed curtains), the desire
60   to actually write poetry could have been construed as proof of mental aberration. But this was my next move, one I effected without being ostracised by my peers because, perhaps, I was also very good at football. Having successfully undergone my masculine rites of passage in the West of Scotland, I could indulge in a little limp-wristed scribbling.

Here again the family situation helped. No one—least of all my father (despite being uninterested in books)—
65   ever questioned the validity of the time I spent arranging words on pieces of paper. I took such tolerance for granted. It was only much later I realised how different it might have been for a working-class boy with ambitions to write. A woman writer-friend told me some years ago of a man she knew who came from a background similar to my own. He was bedevilled by a longing to write plays, much to the embarrassment of his relatives. On one occasion an older brother beat him up severely in an attempt to bring him to his senses and to get
70   him to stop inflicting shame upon the family. Such an attitude had been unimaginable to me in my boyhood.

QUESTIONS FOR PART 1—INTERPRETATION

Marks

(a) From the first paragraph (lines 1–6), quote **two** separate words or phrases which show that the author's memory of his experience is not perfect.

1

(b) Drawing your information from the second paragraph (lines 7–12), give in your own words **two** reasons why it was unusual for the author, as a boy, to be alone in the house.

2

(c) Show how in lines 13–15 the author reinforces the significance of the moment described in the previous paragraphs. In your answer you should refer to **two** of the following: sentence structure; imagery; word choice; tense.

4

(d) Choose **one** of the extended images contained in lines 16–20 and show how effective you find it in describing the boy's awakening.

2

(e) "What I saw in fact was pretty banal." (line 21)

Explain how lines 21–24 ("My father . . . was wonderful.") help you to arrive at the meaning of "banal".

2

(f) Explain fully the part that lines 32–34 play in the structure of the passage as a whole.

3

(g) Explain how lines 35–37 help you to arrive at the meaning of "the ordinary is just the unique in hiding." (line 35)

2

(h) From lines 38–43, give **two** features of the author's home life as a boy which ensured that he encountered a wide variety of language.

2

(i) (i) In your own words, explain why the boy was "astonished" (line 47).

1

    (ii) By referring closely to one example of imagery from "Our house . . . glimpses of living." (lines 44–50), show how effective you find the author's use of this device in conveying the special contribution made by his home to his future career.

3

(j) By referring to lines 51–57, explain the separate roles played by the different members of the boy's family in his developing fascination with language.

3

(k) Look carefully at the sentence beginning, "If books were . . ." (line 58).

    (i) What is the tone of ". . . books were not the most sought-after domestic adjuncts in our housing scheme" (lines 58–59)?

1

    (ii) Select any features of sentence structure and word choice in the rest of the sentence which contribute to this tone and explain how they do so.

2

    (iii) From the rest of the paragraph (lines 59–63), quote a word or a phrase which maintains the tone and briefly explain how it does so.

1

(l) Explain fully the meaning of **two** of the following:

    (i) "going to sleep with the sound of disputation as a lullaby" (line 43);

    (ii) "To this continuing seminar on life" (line 44);

    (iii) "my masculine rites of passage" (line 62).

4

(m) To what extent do you find the anecdote related in lines 67–70 a suitable conclusion to the passage? Justify your view.

2

(n) Drawing your information from line 35 to the end of the passage, give in your own words **five** factors which had a positive influence on McIlvanney's development as a writer.

5

Total marks (40)

READ THE INSTRUCTIONS BEFORE YOU ATTEMPT THIS QUESTION

(i) *Cartoon and slogan*

Do you need any help in crossing
the information superhighway, sir?

"Why use snail-mail when
you can use e-mail?"

Popular slogan

(ii) *Extract from a teenage magazine.*

Q: What is the Internet?

A: **It's simply a collection of computer networks—computers which are linked up with one another all over the world.**

Q: Who uses it?

A: **Anyone who wants to: students, business people—anyone who has a computer and a telephone and a connection device (a modem).**

Q: What do you do with it?

A: **You can use it to advertise (if you're selling something), to ask questions (people will offer information), to find out (you can get into hundreds of libraries and collections all over the world), or just "talk" to other people.**

Q: How big is it?

A: **No one is too sure—it's growing all the time. It's estimated that there will be 250 million users throughout the world by 1999.**

Q: Who owns it—or controls it, then?

A: **No one. It's like a big market place—people bring things along and others look and "buy", if they want to.**

Q: How do I get into it, if I want to?

A: **You'd need a computer, first, of course. You need an ordinary phone line, and then the modem, which connects the computer to the phone line. Finally, you'll need an access system—you pay an annual fee to one of the many companies which offer a way into the system. Then you just go ahead—you can call up any one of millions of users, from the US Library of Congress to a wee guy sitting in a flat in downtown Crieff.**

Q: Wouldn't that cost an awful lot?

A: **Not really. Say you have your computer—and a phone line. You can get a modem for maybe as little as £100; the annual access fee is around £150, and each phone call is charged at the local rate, even if you're wandering about a museum in Australia researching didgeridoos. If that still seems a lot of money, you could use one of the set-ups that are available in schools and colleges, or in some libraries; you could even visit one of the "cybercafes", where you can sit and have a cappuccino and use the machines installed there.**

Q: When can I start?

A: **You can log on any time, man; log on and surf the cyberspace waves till the fat lady sings.**

Q: Eh?

A: **Yes, there is at least one other drawback—you could do with learning the jargon, and it's all American.**

THE INTERNET

The items on pages 6, 7 and 8 relate to the topic of the Internet. Read them carefully.

Your task is to write a report by selecting relevant information and reorganising the material provided. You might find it helpful to consider the following:

(*a*) what the Internet is and how it operates;

(*b*) what may be perceived as the advantages of having access to it;

(*c*) what may be perceived as drawbacks.

You must base your report entirely on the material presented to you, and on any direct inferences you can draw from it. You should use your own words as far as possible. You should take an objective point of view. Write your report in formal, continuous prose. You are likely to be able to complete this task in about 400 words, but there is no penalty for exceeding the length.

You should spend approximately one hour on this part of the paper, which is worth 35 marks.

(iii)   *From the newspapers*

A threat to our basic freedoms?

Of the 11,000 most repeated searches on the Internet, 47% are reported to be for pornographic material. Now the United States-based online service CompuServe has blocked access for its four million users to a sex-oriented area of the Internet.

However, this form of censorship has met with a storm of protest.

"The part that is the greatest threat is that rules will be put up and barriers will be set before we even know what this business (the Internet) is all about and what great opportunities it offers," said Gary Arlen, president of Arlen Communications.

"This is how Nazi Germany and Communist Russia started out—by taking away basic freedoms of the people," argued one mid-westerner who said he had "old-time family values".

"Do we abolish cars because of a few speeders?" complained another incensed user.

The Scotsman

Too much information . . . not enough thought?

I do not deny that the computer can enable students to gain access quickly to information. The trouble is there is now too much information and not enough thought.

An idea is emerging that linking up computers will allow students to unite into a kind of "university of the air", so removing any need for them to meet or live together in one place. The university of the future, according to this argument, will no longer be "campus-dependent".

But the thought of thousands of students sitting alone, all over the country, churning out assignments, is a dreadful distortion of the whole concept of a university.

(iv)   *Some personal views*

(*a*)   It's like everything else to do with computers—the boys monopolise it, and don't let the girls get a look in. It's been estimated that at best 20% of current users are female, but that figure could be as low as 4% according to other research results I've seen. What makes them think it's a "boys' thing", anyway? The whole thing is really male-orientated, too: that crazy jargon they use, and most of the information-providers provide what men are interested in—facts, figures, statistics, graphs, analyses. Then when there is any interaction, any human connection, you get the sexist angle coming in—"What's a nice girl like you doing surfing cyberspace?" I don't waste my time with it now.

(Liz—21—Sociology student)

(*b*)   It's not just for students. I bought our last holiday through it—and I got quite a bargain, too. I was able to call up a company in Seattle and they got me this fantastic safari holiday in Kenya. They sent a video straight to my own computer screen and I was able to see exactly what the hotel was like, what the rooms were like, what the safari was going to be like—I was in control of the video and I could steer the camera wherever I wanted, with the controls on my own keyboard. It was really great. I actually do a lot of my shopping on it now. If I really want, I can shop in Paris, New York, London—without leaving my own home.

(Melanie—37—Public Relations consultant)

(*c*)   I've just been on the Internet—it's great! You can get into university sites in the US where they have masses of stuff. It would take me months to get it through library loans. I've just found a whole lot of material that's connected with some research I did when I was a student. If only I had been able to trace it then! And you can follow up a reference from there to another university library way across the States, right down to the latest research results. There's almost too much; you can't decide where to stop. You want everything at once and then you have so much you can't handle it all. If only I had more time, and three lifetimes, I could begin to get to grips with the possibilities.

(James—48—Maths teacher)

(*d*)   The one incredible benefit is being able to stay in your own home town but still be able to link up with students all over the world. Young people no longer need to flock to the old centres of learning—the centres of learning can come to them! And you could start and stop your education any time you wanted. The freedoms—the power—this Internet gives you are fantastic. We don't really know the full implications yet.

(Garry—19—Media Studies student)

[END OF QUESTION PAPER]

SCOTTISH
CERTIFICATE OF
EDUCATION
1997

TUESDAY, 6 MAY
1.00 PM – 2.35 PM

ENGLISH
HIGHER GRADE
Paper II

There are **two parts** to this paper and you should attempt both parts.

In Part 1, you should attempt **either** Section A (Practical Criticism) **or** Section B (Close Reading of Specified Texts).

In Section A there are two optional questions for Practical Criticism. If you choose Section A, attempt only one of the two Practical Criticism questions.

In Section B there are nine optional questions on Specified Texts. If you choose Section B, attempt only one of the nine Specified Texts questions.

Each option in Part 1 is worth 25 marks.

In Part 2 (Critical Essay), you should attempt **one** question only, taken from any of the Sections A–D.

Your answer to Part 2 should begin on a fresh page.

Each question in Part 2 is worth 30 marks.

NB You must not use, in any part of this paper, the same text(s) as you have used in your Review of Personal Reading.

You must also pay attention to the instruction at the top of each Section in Part 2 about the use of genres and specified texts.

Index of Specified Texts/Authors in Part 1 Section B

1 *Romeo and Juliet*
2 Robert Burns
3 *North and South*
4 *The Devil's Disciple*
5 *The Inheritors*
6 Iain Crichton Smith
7 *Bold Girls*
8 *Sunset Song*
9 Philip Larkin

PART 1

You should spend approximately 45 minutes on this part of the paper.

SECTION A—PRACTICAL CRITICISM

If you choose this Section, attempt <u>either</u> **Option 1 below** <u>or</u> **Option 2, which begins on Page four.**

Option 1

Enter the letter corresponding to each question in the left-hand margin of your answer book.

The following scene from *The Wallace* by Sydney Goodsir Smith occurs at Wallace's trial before the English King after the Scots Lords have betrayed him.

Read the extract carefully and answer the questions which follow on **Page three**.

	KING EDWARD	[*without anger*]: Traitor, rebel, vandal, murderer, What have you to say?
	WALLACE:	I never was a traitor, Edward.
	KING EDWARD:	You have heard the indictment.
5	WALLACE:	I was never liege of Edward, I was never traitor to my King.
	KING EDWARD:	I am your King, you are my liege.
	WALLACE:	The King of Scots was my King.
	KING EDWARD:	I am the King of Scots now, Wallace.
10	WALLACE:	No, sir. Yon's a dream ye had. Ye'll wauken frae it in a wee.
	KING EDWARD:	I know of no other King of Scots.
	WALLACE:	Whose faut is yon?
	KING EDWARD:	That is not decorous in this place.
15	WALLACE:	I didna choose the place, sir. In Scotland decorum isna expeckit Or requirit in an outlaw.
	KING EDWARD:	You are in England now, Wallace.
	WALLACE	[*with a glance at the* SCOTS LORDS]: Forgie me, Majestie. I had forgot.
20		SCOTS LORDS *stir and girn and look uneasy.*
	KING EDWARD:	You are a brave man, Wallace, and I can Respect a warrior; even, perhaps, In the balance, forgive him his Barbarities. You have given me
25		A thought, just now.
	WALLACE:	They are nae bonnie thochts That I can gie, Majestie.
	KING EDWARD:	You may jest. But hearken to me, You have done me great wrong, assuredly,
30		As you have heard at some length. None of this you deny.

	WALLACE:	I deny treason.
	KING EDWARD:	Well, let us leave that by the way for now.
35		I can respect your loyalty too, Wallace.
		I would win it.
	WALLACE:	It's no for winnin,
		Edward, or for sale.
	KING EDWARD:	The war is over now,
		Wallace, finished for ever.
40	WALLACE:	For the saxt time in echt year.

Marks

(a) (i) What possible contradiction is there between the stage direction and the words Edward uses to address Wallace in line 1?   **1**

    (ii) What does Wallace's reply (line 3) suggest about King Edward's accusations?   **2**

(b) Suggest two ways in which the sentence structure of the speeches (lines 4–9) emphasises:

    (i) the conflict between the two men;

    (ii) the personalities of both men.   **4**

(c) What explanation can you suggest for the change in Wallace's speech in line 10?   **2**

(d) (i) In your own words explain what criticism Edward is making (line 14) of Wallace's question (line 13).   **2**

    (ii) Explain how, in lines 15–17, Wallace turns Edward's words to his own advantage.   **2**

(e) (i) Explain the effect of the stage direction on the meaning and the dramatic delivery of Wallace's words (line 19).   **4**

    (ii) What is the dramatic function of the presence of the Scots lords in this extract?   **2**

(f) This scene shows a confrontation between two powerful leaders. By referring closely to their dialogue from line 21 to the end of the passage, justify your choice as to which one wins this war of words.

You should consider how each one expresses his arguments by using such language features as word choice, sentence structure, tone, dialect, humour to express his arguments.   **6**

(25)

SECTION A—PRACTICAL CRITICISM (continued)

Option 2

Enter the letter corresponding to each question in the left-hand margin of your answer book.

Read the Shakespearean sonnet carefully and answer the questions which follow.

SONNET 65

> Since brass, nor stone, nor earth, nor boundless sea,
> But sad mortality o'ersways their power,
> How with this rage shall beauty hold a plea,
4 > Whose action is no stronger than a flower?
> O, how shall summer's honey breath hold out
> Against the wrackful siege of battering days,
> When rocks impregnable are not so stout,
8 > Nor gates of steel so strong, but Time decays?
> O fearful meditation! Where, alack,
> Shall Time's best jewel from Time's chest lie hid?
> Or what strong hand can hold his swift foot back?
12 > Or who his spoil of beauty can forbid?
>   O, none, unless this miracle have might,
>   That in black ink my love may still shine bright.

Marks

(*a*) (i) Consider lines 1–2 and explain, in your own words, what it is that can overpower the items mentioned in line 1.　　1

    (ii) Explain why one of the items might have been selected to illustrate the point being made.　　1

(*b*) (i) Show how the rhythm reinforces the meaning in lines 1–4.　　2

    (ii) Explain fully, in your own words, the contrast which is set out in lines 1–4.　　4

(*c*) (i) Explain the personification in line 5.　　1

    (ii) Show how the idea of the phrase "hold out" is continued in the imagery of lines 6–8.　　2

    (iii) Go on to explain how effective you find the imagery in lines 5–8 in establishing a similar contrast to the one in lines 1–4.　　4

(*d*) What is the "fearful meditation" (line 9)?　　2

(*e*) Show how the use of questions in the poem helps you to appreciate the developing mood or feelings.　　4

(*f*) How satisfying do you find the final lines (13–14) in form and content as a resolution or an answer to the poet's fear expressed throughout the sonnet?　　4

(25)

SECTION B—CLOSE READING OF SPECIFIED TEXTS

If you have chosen to attempt this Section, you should select only ONE extract and answer the questions which follow it.

You should enter the number and the name of the text chosen at the top of the page, and the letter corresponding to each question in the left-hand margin.

You are reminded of the instruction on the front cover about the use of texts.

1. *ROMEO AND JULIET*

Read the extract carefully and answer the questions which follow. The number of marks attached to each question will give a clear indication of the length of answer required.

This extract is taken from Act III Scene 1 of the play.

	TYBALT:	Well, peace be with you sir, here comes my man.
	MERCUTIO:	But I'll be hanged sir, if he wear your livery. Marry go before to field, he'll be your follower; Your worship in that sense may call him man.
5	TYBALT:	Romeo, the love I bear thee can afford No better term than this—thou art a villain.
	ROMEO:	Tybalt, the reason that I have to love thee Doth much excuse the appertaining rage To such a greeting. Villain am I none.
10		Therefore farewell, I see thou knowest me not.
	TYBALT:	Boy, this shall not excuse the injuries That thou hast done me, therefore turn and draw.
	ROMEO:	I do protest I never injuried thee, But love thee better than thou canst devise,
15		Till thou shalt know the reason of my love. And so good Capulet, which name I tender As dearly as my own, be satisfied.
	MERCUTIO:	O calm, dishonourable, vile submission! *Alla stoccata* carries it away.
20		Tybalt, you rat-catcher, will you walk?
	TYBALT:	What wouldst thou have with me?
	MERCUTIO:	Good King of Cats, nothing but one of your nine lives, that I mean to make bold withal, and as you shall use me hereafter, dry-beat the rest of the eight. Will
25		you pluck your sword out of his pilcher by the ears? Make haste, lest mine be about your ears ere it be out.
	TYBALT:	I am for you.
	ROMEO:	Gentle Mercutio, put thy rapier up.
	MERCUTIO:	Come sir, your *passado*.
30	ROMEO:	Draw Benvolio, beat down their weapons. Gentlemen, for shame, forbear this outrage. Tybalt, Mercutio, the Prince expressly hath Forbid this bandying in Verona streets. Hold Tybalt. Good Mercutio.

Marks

(a)   (i)   "... here comes my man." (line 1)

How does your knowledge of the relationship between Tybalt and Romeo help you to understand what Tybalt means by these words?   **2**

(ii)   Explain fully the interpretation Mercutio gives these same words in lines 2–3.   **2**

(b)   By referring to the tone and word order of Tybalt's and Romeo's speeches (lines 5–10), show how a contrast in their attitudes is revealed.   **4**

(c)   (i)   Comment on the use of "boy" in line 11.   **1**

(ii)   Briefly explain "the reason" (line 15) that Romeo has to "love" Tybalt.   **1**

(d)   (i)   By referring to the language of lines 18–20, describe Mercutio's reaction to what has just happened.   **2**

(ii)   By looking closely at the language of lines 22–29, show how two aspects of Mercutio's character are revealed.   **4**

(e)   (i)   What is the immediate consequence of the events in this extract?   **1**

(ii)   Explain how these events can be seen as a turning point in the play. You may consider some of the following features—plot, mood, theme, character development.   **8**

(25)

You are reminded of the instruction on the front cover about the use of texts.

2. ROBERT BURNS

Read carefully the extract from *Address to the Deil* and answer the questions which follow. The number of marks attached to each question will give a clear indication of the length of answer required.

Lang syne, in EDEN'S bonie yard,
When youthfu' lovers first were pair'd,
An' all the Soul of Love they shar'd,
The raptur'd hour,
5   Sweet on the fragrant, flow'ry swaird,
In shady bow'r.

Then you, ye auld, snick-drawing dog!
Ye cam to Paradise incog,
An' play'd on man a cursed brogue,
10   (Black be your fa'!)
An, gied the infant warld a shog,
'Maist ruin'd a'.

D'ye mind that day, when in a bizz
Wi' reeket duds, an' reestet gizz,
15   Ye did present your smoutie phiz,
'Mang better folk,
An' sklented on the *man of Uzz*,
Your spitefu' joke?

An' how ye gat him i' your thrall,
20   An' brak him out o' house an' hal',
While scabs an' botches did him gall,
Wi' bitter claw,
An' lows'd his ill-tongu'd, wicked *Scawl*
Was warst ava?

25   But a' your doings to rehearse,
Your wily snares an' fechtin fierce,
Sin' that day MICHAEL did you pierce,
Down to this time,
Wad ding a' *Lallan* tongue, or *Erse*,
30   In Prose or Rhyme.

An' now, auld *Cloots*, I ken ye're thinkan,
A certain *Bardie's* rantin, drinkin,
Some luckless hour will send him linkan,
To your black pit;
35   But faith! he'll turn a corner jinkan,
An' cheat you yet.

But fare-you-weel, auld *Nickie-ben*!
O wad ye tak a thought an' men'!
Ye aiblins might—I dinna ken—
40   Still hae a *stake*—
I'm wae to think upo' yon den,
Ev'n for your sake!

Marks

(*a*)   (i) By referring closely to the language, describe the picture of Eden presented (lines 1–6).   **2**

    (ii) By referring to two language features in lines 7–12, show how a change in mood is achieved.   **2**

(*b*) Show how Burns uses two different sound effects in lines 13–18 to undermine the threatening nature of the Devil.   **4**

(*c*) How is the idea of the Devil being "*spitefu'*" (line 18) developed in lines 19–24?   **2**

(*d*) Explain how stanza 5 acts as a turning point in the poet's line of thought.   **3**

(*e*)   (i) By referring to the forms of address used in lines 31–42, show that there has been a change in the attitude of the poet to the Devil.   **2**

    (ii) Show how this change in attitude is further developed in lines 37–42.   **2**

(*f*) Choose another poem by Burns that has a religious or moral theme. With close reference to the text, show how he develops the theme in the poem you have chosen.   **8**

    (25)

You are reminded of the instruction on the front cover about the use of texts.

3.   *NORTH AND SOUTH*

Read the extract carefully and answer the questions which follow. The number of marks attached to each question will give a clear indication of the length of answer required.

The extract is taken from the chapter entitled "A Blow and its Consequences".

"For God's sake! do not damage your cause by this violence. You do not know what you are doing."
She strove to make her words distinct.

A sharp pebble flew by her, grazing forehead and cheek, and drawing a blinding sheet of light before her
eyes. She lay like one dead on Mr Thornton's shoulder. Then he unfolded his arms, and held her
5   encircled in one for an instant:

"You do well!" said he. "You come to oust the innocent stranger. You fall—you hundreds—on one
man; and when a woman comes before you, to ask you for your own sakes to be reasonable creatures,
your cowardly wrath falls upon her! You do well!" They were silent while he spoke. They were
watching, open-eyed, and open-mouthed, the thread of dark-red blood which wakened them up from
10 their trance of passion. Those nearest the gate stole out ashamed; there was a movement through all the
crowd—a retreating movement. Only one voice cried out: "Th' stone were meant for thee; but thou
wert sheltered behind a woman!"

Mr Thornton quivered with rage. The blood-flowing had made Margaret conscious—dimly, vaguely
conscious. He placed her gently on the door-step, her head leaning against the frame.

15 "Can you rest there?" he asked. But without waiting for her answer, he went slowly down the steps
right into the middle of the crowd. "Now kill me, if it is your brutal will. There is no woman to shield
me here. You may beat me to death—you will never move me from what I have determined upon—not
you!" He stood amongst them, with his arms folded, in precisely the same attitude as he had been in on
the steps.

20 But the retrograde movement towards the gate had begun—as unreasoningly, perhaps as blindly, as the
simultaneous anger. Or, perhaps, the idea of the approach of the soldiers, and the sight of that pale,
upturned face, with closed eyes, still and sad as marble, though the tears welled out of the long
entanglement of eyelashes, and dropped down; and, heavier, slower plash than even tears, came the drip
of blood from her wound. Even the most desperate—Boucher himself—drew back, faltered away,
25 scowled, and finally went off, muttering curses on the master, who stood in his unchanging attitude,
looking after their retreat with defiant eyes. The moment that retreat had changed into a flight (as it
was sure from its very character to do), he darted up the steps to Margaret.

Marks

(*a*) Give a brief description of the industrial events which have led to the gathering of the angry crowd outside Mr Thornton's house.   **2**

(*b*) State what differing views Margaret and Mr Thornton have on the merits of the strike. Support each view with evidence from this extract.   **2**

(*c*) (i)   Show how the language used by Mr Thornton in his speech (lines 6–18) demonstrates his mood.   **2**

    (ii) How do his actions described in lines 18–19 reinforce this mood?   **1**

(*d*) The detailed description of Margaret's face (lines 21–24) is seen to create fear or sympathy in the strikers. Comment on two literary techniques used by the author to achieve this effect.   **4**

(*e*) Throughout the extract there are several occasions when the movement of the mob is described. Referring closely to the text, trace these movements, showing how they reflect the moods of the mob during this incident.   **4**

(*f*) Show how this incident is central to two of the main themes of the novel. You should refer to events both before and after this extract in your answer.   **10**

                                                                    (25)

You are reminded of the instruction on the front cover about the use of texts.

4. *THE DEVIL'S DISCIPLE*

Read the extract carefully and answer the questions which follow. The number of marks attached to each question will give a clear indication of the length of answer required.

This extract is from Act 1.

	MRS DUDGEON:	[*rising and confronting him*] Silence your blasphemous tongue. I will bear no more of this. Leave my house.
	RICHARD:	How do you know it's your house until the will is read? [*They look at one another for a moment with intense hatred; and then she sinks, checkmated, into her chair. Richard goes boldly up past Anderson to the window, where he takes the railed chair in his hand.*] Ladies and gentlemen: as the eldest son of my late father, and the unworthy head of this household, I bid you welcome. By your leave, Minister Anderson: by your leave, Lawyer Hawkins. The head of the table for the head of the family. [*He places the chair at the table between the minister and the attorney; sits down between them; and addresses the assembly with a presidential air.*] We meet on a melancholy occasion: a father dead! an uncle actually hanged, and probably damned. [*He shakes his head deploringly. The relatives freeze with horror.*] That's right: pull your longest faces [*his voice suddenly sweetens gravely as his glance lights on Essie*] provided only there is hope in the eyes of the child. [*Briskly*] Now then, Lawyer Hawkins: business, business. Get on with the will, man.
	TITUS:	Do not let yourself be ordered or hurried, Mr Hawkins.
	HAWKINS:	[*very politely and willingly*] Mr Dudgeon means no offence, I feel sure. I will not keep you one second, Mr Dudgeon. Just while I get my glasses—[*he fumbles for them. The Dudgeons look at one another with misgiving.*]
20	RICHARD:	Aha! They notice your civility, Mr Hawkins. They are prepared for the worst. A glass of wine to clear your voice before you begin. [*He pours out one for him and hands it; then pours one for himself.*]
	HAWKINS:	Thank you, Mr Dudgeon. Your good health, sir.
25	RICHARD:	Yours, sir. [*With the glass half way to his lips, he checks himself, giving a dubious glance at the wine, and adds, with quaint intensity*] Will anyone oblige me with a glass of water?
		Essie, who has been hanging on his every word and movement, rises stealthily and slips out behind Mrs Dudgeon through the bedroom door, returning presently with a jug and going out of the house as quietly as possible.
30	HAWKINS:	The will is not exactly in proper legal phraseology.
	RICHARD:	No: my father died without the consolations of the law.
	HAWKINS:	Good again, Mr Dudgeon, good again. [*Preparing to read*] Are you ready, sir?
	RICHARD:	Ready, aye ready. For what we are about to receive, may the Lord make us truly thankful. Go ahead.
35	HAWKINS:	[*reading*] "This is the last will and testament of me Timothy Dudgeon on my deathbed at Nevinstown on the road from Springtown to Websterbridge on this twenty-fourth day of September, one thousand seven hundred and seventy seven. I hereby revoke all former wills made by me and declare that I am of sound mind and know well what I am doing and that this is my real will according to my own wish and affections."
40		
	RICHARD:	[*glancing at his mother*] Aha!

HAWKINS:		*[shaking his head]* Bad phraseology, sir, wrong phraseology. "I give and bequeath a hundred pounds to my younger son Christopher Dudgeon, fifty pounds to be paid to him on the day of his marriage to Sarah Wilkins if she will have him, and ten pounds on the birth of each of his children up to the number of five."
45		
RICHARD:		How if she won't have him?
CHRISTY:		She will if I have fifty pounds.
RICHARD:		Good, my brother. Proceed.
HAWKINS:		"I give and bequeath to my wife Annie Dudgeon, born Annie Primrose"—you see he did not know the law, Mr Dudgeon: your mother was not born Annie: she was christened so—"an annuity of fifty-two pounds a year for life *[Mrs Dudgeon, with all eyes on her, holds herself convulsively rigid]* to be paid out of the interest on her own money"—there's a way to put it, Mr Dudgeon! Her own money!
50		
MRS DUDGEON:		A very good way to put God's truth. It was every penny my own. Fifty-two pounds a year!
55		
HAWKINS:		"And I recommend her for her goodness and piety to the forgiving care of her children, having stood between them and her as far as I could to the best of my ability."
MRS DUDGEON:		And this is my reward! *[Raging inwardly]* You know what I think, Mr Anderson: you know the word I gave to it.
60		
ANDERSON:		It cannot be helped, Mrs Dudgeon. We must take what comes to us. *[To Hawkins.]* Go on, sir.
HAWKINS:		"I give and bequeath my house at Websterbridge with the land belonging to it and all the rest of my property soever to my eldest son and heir, Richard Dudgeon."

Marks

(a) Explain briefly the circumstances that have led to the remarks in lines 1–2.

2

(b) By referring closely to lines 3–15, show how Richard's actions help to reinforce the dramatic impact of his speech.

3

(c) Identify one dramatic device in lines 16–26 and explain how Shaw uses it to build up the tension in the scene.

2

(d) Describe two aspects of Hawkins's personality that are revealed in lines 30–32. You should support your answer with close reference to the text.

4

(e) By referring closely to the contents of the will (lines 35–64), comment on what we learn of the relationship of Mr Dudgeon to his wife and to each of his sons.

3

(f) (i) This extract could be regarded as typical of the set-piece situation expected in a melodrama. Choose one other scene from the play and describe its melodramatic features.

3

(ii) To what extent do you regard the term "melodrama" as a valid description of the play as a whole? You should consider some of the following features: characterisation, dialogue, theme, action.

8

(25)

You are reminded of the instruction on the front cover about the use of texts.

5. *THE INHERITORS*

Read the extract carefully and answer the questions which follow. The number of marks attached to each question will give a clear indication of the length of answer required.

In this extract from Chapter 3 the people need to find food.

"This is old honey from the time when we went down to the sea. We must find more food for the others. Come!"

But Lok was thrusting the butt in again for joy of Liku's eating, the sight of her belly and the memory of honey. Fa went away down the apron of rock, following the mist as it sucked back to the plain. She
5   lowered herself over the edge and was out of sight. Then they heard her cry out. Liku scrambled up on Lok's back and he flitted down the apron towards the cry with his thorn bush at the ready. At the edge of the apron was a jagged gully that led out to the open country. Fa was crouching in the mouth of this gully, looking out over the grass and heather of the plain. Lok raced to her. Fa was trembling slightly and raised on her toes. There were two yellowish creatures out there, their legs hidden by the brown
10   bushes of heather, near enough for her to see their eyes. They were prick-eared animals, roused by her voice from their business and standing now at gaze. Lok slid Liku from his back.

"Climb."

Liku scrambled up the side of the gully and squatted, higher in the air than Lok could reach. The yellow creatures showed their teeth.

15   "Now!"

Lok stole forward holding his thorn bush sideways. Fa circled out to his left. She carried a natural blade of stone in either hand. The two hyenas moved closer together and snarled. Fa suddenly jerked her right hand round and the stone thumped the bitch in the ribs. The bitch yelped then ran howling. Lok shot forward, swinging the thorn bush, and thrust the spines at the dog's snarling muzzle. Then
20   the two beasts were out of reach, talking evilly and afraid. Lok stood between them and the kill.

"Be quick, I smell cat."

Fa was already down on her knees, struggling with the limp body.

"A cat has sucked all her blood. There is no blame. The yellow ones have not even reached the liver."

She was tearing fiercely at the doe's belly with the flake of stone. Lok brandished his thorn bush at the
25   hyenas.

"There is much food for all the people."

He could hear how Fa grunted and gasped as she tore at the furred skin and the guts.

"Be quick."

"I cannot."

30   The hyenas, having finished their evil talk, were circling forward to left and right. Shadows flitted across Lok as he faced them from two great birds that were floating in the air.

"Take the doe to the rock."

Fa began to lug at the doe, then cried out in anger at the hyenas. Lok backed to her, bent down, seized the doe by the leg. He began to drag the body heavily towards the gully, brandishing the thorn bush the
35   while. Fa seized a foreleg and hauled too. The hyenas followed them, keeping always just out of reach. The people got the doe into the narrow entrance to the gully just below Liku and the two birds floated down. Fa began to slash again with her splinter of stone. Lok found a boulder which he could use hammer-wise. He began to pound at the body, breaking out the joints. Fa was grunting with excitement. Lok talked as his great hands tore and twisted and snapped the sinews. All the time the
40   hyenas ran to and fro. The birds drifted in and settled on the rock opposite Liku so that she slithered down to Lok and Fa.

The doe was wrecked and scattered. Fa split open her belly, slit the complicated stomach and spilt the sour cropped grass and broken shoots on the earth. Lok beat in the skull to get at the brain and levered open the mouth to wrench away the tongue. They filled the stomach with tit-bits and twisted up the
45   guts so that the stomach became a floppy bag.

All the while, Lok talked between his grunts.

"This is bad. This is very bad."

Now the limbs were smashed and bloodily jointed Liku crouched by the doe eating the piece of liver that Fa had given her. The air between the rocks was forbidding with violence and sweat, with the rich
50   smell of meat and wickedness.

"Quick! Quick!"

Fa could not have told him what she feared; the cat would not come back to a drained kill. It would be already half a day's journey away over the plain, hanging round the skirts of the herd, perhaps racing forward to sink its sabres in the neck of another victim and suck the blood. Yet there was a kind of
55   darkness in the air under the watching birds.

Marks

(a)   What differences in their characters are revealed by Fa's words and Lok's actions in lines 1–4 down to "... honey"?   **4**

(b)   Read again from "Fa began ..." (line 37) down to "... floppy bag." (line 45)

By referring closely to the language of these lines, explain what kind of atmosphere is created.   **4**

(c)   By close reference to the text, show how Golding makes the business of food:

    (i)   a matter of urgency;   **2**

    (ii)   a matter of morality.   **4**

(d)   By referring to examples from this extract, show how the people's use of language reflects their stage of development.   **3**

(e)   Lok's relationship with Liku is one of the most tender features of the novel.

    (i)   Provide from this extract two pieces of evidence for this statement.   **2**

    (ii)   By referring to other parts of the novel, show how the relationship between Lok and Liku helps you to become involved in the fate of the people.   **6**

        (25)

You are reminded of the instruction on the front cover about the use of texts.

6.   IAIN CRICHTON SMITH

Read the poem carefully and answer the questions which follow. The number of marks attached to each question will give a clear indication of the length of answer required.

"You'll take a bath"

> "And now you'll take a bath," she'd always say,
> just when I was leaving, to keep me back.
> At the second turning of the stony stair
> the graffiti were black letters in a book
> 5 misspelt and menacing. As I drove away
> she'd wave from the window. How could I always bear
> to be her knight abandoning her to her tower
> each second Sunday, a ghost that was locked fast
> in a Council scheme, where radios played all day
> 10 unknown raw music, and young couples brought
> friends home to midnight parties, and each flower
> in the grudging garden died in trampled clay.
>
> Standing by her headstone in the mild
> city of bell-less doors, I feel the sweat
> 15 stink my fresh shirt out, as each gravelly path
> becomes a road, long lost, in a bad bet.
> Once more I see the dirty sleepy child.
> "The water's hot enough. You'll have a bath."
>
> And almost I am clean but for that door
> 20 so blank and strong, imprinted with her name
> as that far other in the scheme was once,
> and 'scheme' becomes a mockery, and a shame,
> in this neat place, where each vase has its flower,
> and the arching willow its maternal stance.

Marks

(a)   What do the opening two lines suggest about the relationship between the two people in the poem?   **3**

(b)   (i)   Show how aspects of fantasy or fairytale are conveyed in lines 3–8.   **2**

(ii)   How does this contrast with the picture presented in lines 9–12?   **2**

(iii)   What does the contrast suggest about the poet's feelings towards the situation?   **2**

(c)   (i)   Examine the significance of the "door" image which appears throughout verses 2 and 3. Explain how well you think it conveys the poet's feelings.   **4**

(ii)   How are these feelings further explored in verses 2 and 3 (lines 13–24)?   **4**

(d)   By referring to at least one other poem by Iain Crichton Smith, show how he describes and/or examines the gulf that may exist in relationships between people.   **8**

(25)

7. BOLD GIRLS

Read the extract carefully and answer the questions which follow. The number of marks attached to each question will give a clear indication of the length of answer required.

In the following extract, the girls are having a night out.

NORA: You're bringing shame on this family, Cassie.

CASSIE: Well I won't be the first.

NORA: What do you mean?

CASSIE: Our Martin was never too good at keeping his belt buckle fastened, was he?

5 NORA: Your brother was a good boy, the best boy a mother ever—

CASSIE (*interrupting*): Well, you tell that to the wee girl in Turf Lodge.

Marie crumples another sheet of paper.

Oh she just missed it!

NORA: That was not Martin's child.

10 CASSIE: Oh it just borrowed that nose and that red hair off another friend of the family did it? [*Peering*] A magi-mix, oh it'd be great if she got that.

NORA: I asked her to her face, I said, if you can look me in the eye and swear by the Virgin that this is my grandchild I'll not see you short, just look me in the eye and tell me.

CASSIE: Forty-five pounds! Marie! [*She mimes*] Forty-five pounds!

15 NORA: And all she said was, I'm not wanting your money, Mrs Ryan.

CASSIE: Do you know you never put a plate of food in front of me before he had his?

NORA: She was nothing be a wee hoor.

Marie holds up her sheet.

CASSIE: Oh she's put eighty-nine ninety-nine. Oh Marie!

20 NORA: What has food got to do with it?

CASSIE: The only time you gave me food before him was when I was to serve him. I never *once* got my dinner before he'd his in his mouth. Not *once*.

NORA: What are you talking about Cassie?

MARIE: I've got it! [*She waves at Nora and Cassie excitedly*]

25 CASSIE: Oh Mummy! She's won the magi-mix!

Marie stands with her hands up in triumph then stares as:

Deirdre walks over the dance floor to Marie carrying her prize.

There is ragged applause.

Deirdre hands the big box over with a model's grin.

30 MARIE: Thanks.

Deirdre turns and smiles at the applause.

Marie wanders to the side of the dance floor where Nora and Cassie are waiting for her.

CASSIE: Was that your white top, Marie?

MARIE: It looked like it. It looked like my earrings as well.

35 NORA: Did you not used to have a pair of white trousers like that, Marie?

MARIE: I did. They were exactly like that.

NORA: That wee girl is trouble.

CASSIE [*moving towards her*]: And I'm going to find out what kind.

MARIE: Cassie, wait.

40 *Marie catches Cassie's arm.*

She's not going anywhere.

CASSIE: Marie, when will you stand up for yourself? You're a mug! That girl's making a fool of you!

MARIE: And when I get the chance I'll hear what she has to say but it won't be here with half the town hearing it as well Cassie!

45   *Cassie hesitates.*

NORA: Well I'm dry, I think we should get ourselves another drink.

MARIE: That's a great idea, Nora. What'll you have?

NORA: No, no, we'll use the kitty, like before.

CASSIE: I'll get them.

50   MARIE: No, I'll do it, Cassie.

CASSIE: *I'll* get them.

Marie and Nora sit down.

Lighting change

			Marks
(*a*)	(i)	Explain briefly how tension is introduced into this scene in the opening line.	2
	(ii)	By examining carefully lines 2–25, show how the tension is developed.	4
(*b*)	(i)	Explain fully the dramatic effects achieved by Deirdre's role and appearance in this scene.	5
	(ii)	Deirdre has several roles in this play. Explain what two of these roles are, supporting what you say with references to other scenes in the play.	4
(*c*)	(i)	"Your brother was a good boy, the best boy a mother ever—" (line 5) What does this line reveal about Nora's character?	2
	(ii)	By referring to this extract and to elsewhere in the play, show to what extent you agree with the image of men which emerges. Your argument should include substantial support from the play as a whole.	8
			(25)

You are reminded of the instruction on the front cover about the use of texts.

8. *SUNSET SONG*

Read the extract carefully and answer the questions which follow. The number of marks attached to each question will give a clear indication of the length of answer required.

Chris's brother, Will, visits her in Blawearie.

And when he was alone with Chris that evening and she told him about Ewan down training in Lanark, he said Ewan was either soft or daft or both. *Why did you marry the dour devil, Chris? Did he make you or were you going to have a bairn?* And Chris didn't feel affronted, it was Will that asked, he'd treat her just the same if she owned up to a fatherless bairn once a year, or twice, if it came to that. So she shook
5   her head, *It was just because he was to me as Mollie to you,* and Will nodded to that, *Ah, well, we can't help when it gets that way. Mind when you wanted to know . . . ?* And they stood and laughed in the evening, remembering that, and they walked arm in arm up and down the road and Chris forgot all her worries remembering the days when she and Will were bairns together, and the dourness and the loveliness then, and Will asked *Do you mind when we slept together—that last time we did it when the old man had*
10   *near killed me up in the barn?* And his face grew dark, he still couldn't forgive, he said that folk who ill-treated their children deserved to be shot, father had tormented and spoiled him out of sheer cruelty when he was young. But Chris said nothing to that, remembering the day of father's funeral and how she had wept by his grave in Kinraddie kirkyard.

But she knew she could never tell Will of that, he'd never understand, and they spoke of other things,
15   Will of the Argentine and the life out there, and the smell of the sun and the warm weather and the fruit and flowers and flame of life below the Southern Cross. Chris said *But you'll come back, you and Mollie, to bide in Scotland again?* and Will laughed, he seemed still a mere lad in spite of his foreign French uniform, *Havers, who'd want to come back to this country? It's dead or it's dying—and a damned good job!*

And, daftly, Chris felt a sudden thrust of anger through her heart at that; and then she looked round
20   Kinraddie in the evening light, seeing it so quiet and secure and still, thinking of the seeds that pushed up their shoots from a thousand earthy mouths. Daft of Will to say that: Scotland lived, she could never die, the land would outlast them all, their wars and their Argentines, and the winds come sailing over the Grampians still with their storms and rain and the dew that ripened the crops—long and long after all their little vexings in the evening light were dead and done. And her thoughts went back to the
25   kirkyard, she asked Will would he like to come to the kirk next day, she hadn't been there herself for a year.

He looked surprised and then laughed *You're not getting religious, are you?* as though she had taken to drink. And Chris said *No,* and then thought about that, time to think for once in the pother of the days with Blawearie so quiet above them, young Ewan and old Brigson asleep. And she said *I don't believe*
30   *they were ever religious, the Scots folk, Will—not really religious like Irish or French or all the rest in the history books. They've never BELIEVED. It's just been a place to collect and argue, the kirk, and criticize God.* And Will yawned, he said maybe, he didn't care one way or the other himself, Mollie in the Argentine had taken up with the Catholics, and faith! she was welcome if she got any fun.

Marks

(a) Explain briefly why Will has returned to Blawearie at this time.   **1**

(b) By close reference to the text, show what aspects of Will's character are revealed in the first paragraph. (lines 1–13)   **4**

(c) Look again at paragraphs 2 and 3 (lines 14–26). Will talks of the Argentine and Chris is led to consider Scotland itself.

Show how the contrasting feelings of Will and Chris towards Scotland are revealed by examining such aspects as:

  (i)   sentence structure;

  (ii) word choice;

  (iii) narrative voice;

  (iv) dialogue;

  (v)   imagery.   **6**

(d) Chris states that the Scots folk were never truly religious, "*not really religious like Irish or French or all the rest in the history books*". (lines 30–31)

By referring to two characters in the novel, show what evidence there is to support this.   **6**

(e) Discuss the effects of the outside world on the enclosed world of Kinraddie. You should refer to the novel as a whole.   **8**

(25)

You are reminded of the instruction on the front cover about the use of texts.

9. PHILIP LARKIN

Read carefully the extract from *Church Going* and answer the questions which follow. The number of marks attached to each question will give a clear indication of the length of answer required.

CHURCH GOING

> Once I am sure there's nothing going on
> I step inside, letting the door thud shut.
> Another church: matting, seats, and stone,
> And little books; sprawlings of flowers, cut
> 5   For Sunday, brownish now; some brass and stuff
> Up at the holy end; the small neat organ;
> And a tense, musty, unignorable silence,
> Brewed God knows how long. Hatless, I take off
> My cycle-clips in awkward reverence,
>
> 10   Move forward, run my hand around the font.
> From where I stand, the roof almost new—
> Cleaned, or restored? Someone would know: I don't.
> Mounting the lectern, I peruse a few
> Hectoring large-scale verses, and pronounce
> 15   "Here endeth" much more loudly than I'd meant.
> The echoes snigger briefly. Back at the door
> I sign the book, donate an Irish sixpence,
> Reflect the place was not worth stopping for.
>
> Yet stop I did: in fact I often do,
> 20   And always end much at a loss like this,
> Wondering what to look for; wondering, too,
> When churches fall completely out of use
> What we shall turn them into, if we shall keep
> A few cathedrals chronically on show,
> 25   Their parchment, plate and pyx in locked cases,
> And let the rest rent-free to rain and sheep.
> Shall we avoid them as unlucky places?

Marks

(a)　(i)　Describe briefly the attitude to the church presented in stanza 1. (lines 1–9)　　2

　　　(ii)　Show how the word choice and sentence structure of stanza 1 help to support this attitude.　　4

　　　(iii)　Show how the structure and positioning of "Yet stop I did:" (line 19) help to introduce a shift in attitude.　　2

(b)　Choose any three of the following expressions, and explain what each contributes to the tone of the poem as a whole.

　　　(i)　"Another" (line 3);

　　　(ii)　"Hectoring" (line 14);

　　　(iii)　"snigger" (line 16);

　　　(iv)　"donate" (line 17);

　　　(v)　"chronically" (line 24).　　6

(c)　By referring to the ideas of the final two stanzas of **the complete poem**, show how the poet responds to the questions which he raises in this extract.　　5

(d)　It has been suggested that nearly all of Larkin's poetry is cynical. Explain to what extent you would agree with this suggestion, by referring in detail to any other poem by Larkin.　　6

(25)

PART 2—CRITICAL ESSAY

Attempt ONE question only, taken from any of the Sections A to D.

In all Sections you may use Scottish texts.

You should spend about 50 minutes on this part of the paper.

Begin your answer on a fresh page.

If you use a Specified Text as the basis for your Critical Essay, you must not rely ONLY on any extract printed in Part 1 in this paper. If you attempt Section C—Poetry, you should note the additional instruction at the head of Section C.

SECTION A—DRAMA

> If you have answered on a play in the Specified Text option in Part 1 of the paper, you must not attempt a question from this Drama Section.
>
> In your answer in this Section you should, where relevant, refer to such features as dialogue, characterisation, plot, theme, scene, climax, style, structure.

1. "The enemy within."
   Consider a character from a Shakespearean tragedy and show to what extent you feel that the forces which defeat the character come from "within".

2. In many plays the element of suspense is achieved by a gradual revelation of information or truths important to the resolution of the drama. Show that this happens in any such play. (You should beware of simply recounting the plot.)

3. Select one decision which is important in the development of a play you have studied. Show to what extent the character(s) concerned in making the decision acted in a way which you expected, or which surprised you.

4. Choose a play which explores the status of women in society and show to what extent they are seen as victims or as dominant figures.

5. Audience involvement is a technique used in the theatre. In any play you have both studied and seen in stage performance, what devices were used to involve the audience? How effectively did these devices involve you?

SECTION B—PROSE

> **If you have answered on a prose work in the Specified Text option in Part 1 of the paper, you must not attempt a question from this Prose Section.**
>
> **In your answer in this Section you should, where relevant, refer to such features as setting, theme, characterisation, plot, content, style, structure, language, narrative stance, symbolism.**

6. Some novels are written on the grand scale—varied characters, multiple settings, complex plots. From any such novel, choose one of these ingredients, and show to what extent it increased or decreased your appreciation of the novel.

7. Choose one minor but important character from a novel or short story. Give a brief account of his or her part in the plot, and show how important he or she is in affecting the actions and reactions of one of the main characters.

8. Short story writers cannot afford to waste time on unnecessary detail. Considering one short story, show how the choice of significant detail is used to increase your understanding of character, plot and theme.

9. Choose a work of non-fiction which seems to you to have literary merit. Say why the style appeals to you, and show what techniques the author has used to create this appeal.

SECTION C—POETRY

> **If you have answered on a poem in the Specified Text option in Part 1 of the paper, you must not attempt a question from this Poetry Section. You may not base an answer on Burns's "Address to the Deil", Crichton Smith's "You'll Take a Bath" or Larkin's "Church Going".**
>
> **In your answer in this Section you should, where relevant, refer to such features as rhyme, rhythm, word-choice, language, sound, imagery, symbolism, style, structure.**

10. Choose a poem which appealed to you because it is striking. Show which techniques the poet has used to capture your interest and engage your feelings.

11. One of the characteristics of Scottish poetry is its use of humour or satire to deflate pomposity or to attack hypocrisy or simply to ridicule. By referring to one Scottish poem, show how effective you find the use of humour or satire or both.

12. In a successful dramatic monologue the "voice" of the speaker is an important element. Show how particular features of the language used by the speaker are effective in revealing the speaker's personality to the audience.

13. Often a poem has as its stimulus an incident or moment in the poet's everyday experience. Show how the poet uses her/his own experience and by skilful use of poetic techniques makes it important to a wider readership.

SECTION D—MASS MEDIA

If your Review of Personal Reading is based entirely on a radio, television or film script, you must not attempt a question from this Mass Media Section.

---

14. From any film, choose a sequence which communicates important ideas or information in a subtle or a dramatic way. Explain the importance of the ideas or information and by closely referring to mise-en-scene, montage and soundtrack, show how the subtlety or drama is achieved.

15. Choose a film which you consider to be typical of a particular genre, or one which you believe bears the hallmark of a particular director. By referring to key elements, justify your choice.

16. "Many people condemn stereotypes, but they can be very useful."

    By referring to a variety of texts which contain stereotyped representations, show to what extent you agree with this view.

17. Choose a text which represents women or men or a particular social class or an institution in a way which you found provocative. By closely referring to the text, explain how this representation was constructed and in what ways you found it thought-provoking.

18. Choose a television drama which has been adapted from a work of prose. To what extent do you consider the television version has successfully captured particular features of the original text? (In your answer you may wish to consider such features as setting, characters, mood, tone, point of view, theme.)

19. Choose a television series or serial which successfully targets a particular audience. Identify this audience and go on to explain fully how the series or serial satisfies its needs and tastes.

[END OF QUESTION PAPER]

SCOTTISH
CERTIFICATE OF
EDUCATION
1998

TUESDAY, 5 MAY
9.15 AM – 11.20 AM

ENGLISH
HIGHER GRADE
Paper I

There are **two parts** to this paper, Part 1 (Interpretation) and Part 2 (Report). You should attempt both parts.

Part 1 (Interpretation), on pages 2, 3 and 4, is worth 40 marks. There are two passages, with questions following. Use the left-hand margin of the answer book to indicate clearly the questions attempted.

Part 2 (Report), on pages 6, 7 and 8, is worth 35 marks. You should begin your Report on a fresh page of the answer book.

PART 1—INTERPRETATION

Attempt all of Part 1. You should spend approximately 1 hour on this part of the paper, including reading time. There are TWO passages and questions.

Read both passages carefully and then answer all the questions which follow on page four. **Use your own words whenever possible and particularly when you are instructed to do so.** The number of marks attached to each question will give some indication of the kind of answer required.

It is important that you read both passages before you attempt to answer any of the questions.

The first passage, by the distinguished and controversial journalist, John Pilger, appeared in a national newspaper in 1991. The second passage is an extract from Joseph Conrad's short story, "An Outpost of Progress", which was written in the 1890s.

PASSAGE 1

INFORMATION IS POWER

On the day that media tycoon Robert Maxwell died, an estimated 6,000 people were killed in a typhoon in the Philippines, most of them in one town. Maxwell's death dominated the British
5 media. It made an intriguing story, with few facts. Speculation and offerings by former retainers were unrelenting. His yacht was described in all its opulent detail; there was the bed the man had slept in and the crystal he and potentates had drunk
10 from. It was said that he consumed £60,000 worth of caviar in a year. And there was the man himself: in shorts, in shades, in a turban, with Elton John on the sports pages.

The death of the Filipinos, the equivalent of the
15 sudden extinction of a Welsh mining village, with many more children killed than at the Aberfan disaster in 1966, was mentioned in passing, if at all. On the BBC's *Nine O'Clock News* Maxwell was the first item; the disaster in the Philippines was one of
20 the last in a round-up of "fillers".

In one sense, the two events were connected. Maxwell embodied the new age of imperialist wealth: of triumphant rapacity based on asset-stripping, "off-shore" secrecies, and, above all,
25 money-making from debt. The people who were swept to their deaths at Ormoc on the island of Leyte were also part of the new age. In an area of no previous experience of natural calamity, most of them died in flooding and mud slides that may well
30 have been the result of deforestation. "It's a man-made disaster abetted by nature," said Leyte's governor.

With almost half their national budget committed to paying the interest on debt owed to the World
35 Bank, the International Monetary Fund (IMF) and Western commercial banks, Filipinos are raping their beautiful country in order to export anything that brings in dollars and yen. Coral reefs are poisoned with cyanide to provide goldfish for
40 the goldfish bowls of America. Forests are illegally logged to satisfy a Japan long ago stripped of trees.

This is not news, just as the deaths of the victims are, at most, news of minor importance. "Small earthquake: not many dead" is not quite the joke it used to be. Natural disasters in the Third World 45 are reported; it is the manner of the reporting, and the subtext, that helps to secure for the majority of humanity the marginal place the world's media allots them. A typhoon, an earthquake, a war: and they are news of a fleeting kind, emerging solely as 50 victims, accepting passively their predicament as a precondition for Western acknowledgement and charity.

Consider the strictly controlled Western perspective of Africa. The fact that Africa's 55 recurring famines and extreme poverty have political causes rooted in the West is not regarded as news. How many of us were aware during 1985—the year of the Ethiopian famine and of "Live Aid"—that the hungriest countries in Africa 60 gave twice as much money to *us* in the West as we gave to them: billions of dollars to our banks and finance houses just in interest payments on national debt?

We were shown terrible television pictures of 65 children dying and we were not told of the part our financial institutions had played in their deaths. This also was not news. The camera was allowed to dictate a false neutrality, as is often the case, with the reporter playing the role of concerned innocent 70 bystander and caption writer. This "neutrality" is commonly known, with unintended irony, as "objectivity". Yet in truth, it merely reinforces the West's beloved stereotype of Third World dependence. 75

This was illustrated when a group of London schoolchildren was asked for views of the Third World: several of them wrote, "Hell". None of them could provide a coherent picture of actual people. The majority of humanity are not 80 news, merely mute and incompetent stick figures that flit across the television screen. They do not

argue or fight back. They are not brave. They do
not have vision. They do not conceive models of
85 development that suit *them*. They do not form
community and other grass-roots organisations
that seek to surmount the obstacles to a better life.

Never in the Western media is there a celebration
of the survival, the resourcefulness and humanity
of those who live in the Third World; nowhere is 90
there mention of the generosity of the poorest, of
the capacity for altruism of those who have
nothing, of the wisdom, endurance and tenacity of
people displaced from forests, hills or pastures by
western-inspired patterns of development. 95

(John Pilger)

PASSAGE 2

AN OUTPOST OF PROGRESS

Kayerts and Carlier lived like blind men in a large
room, aware only of what came in contact with
them (and of that only imperfectly), but unable to
see the general aspect of things. The river, the
5 forest, all the great land throbbing with life, were
like a great emptiness. Even the brilliant sunshine
disclosed nothing intelligible. Things appeared
and disappeared before their eyes in an
unconnected and aimless kind of way. The river
10 seemed to come from nowhere and go nowhither.
It flowed through a void.

Out of that void, at times, came canoes, and men
with spears in their hands would suddenly crowd
the yard of the trading post. They were naked,
15 glossy black, ornamented with snowy shells and
glistening brass wire, perfect of limb. They made
an uncouth babbling noise when they spoke,
moved in a stately manner, and sent quick, wild
glances out of their startled, never-resting eyes.
20 Those warriors would squat in long rows, four or
more deep, before the verandah, while their chiefs
bargained for hours with Makola over an elephant
tusk.

Kayerts sat on his chair and looked down on the
25 proceedings, understanding nothing. He stared at
them with his round blue eyes, called out to
Carlier, "Here, look! look at that fellow there—and
that other one, to the left. Did you ever see such a
face? Oh, the funny brute!"

30 Carlier, smoking native tobacco in a short wooden
pipe, would swagger up twirling his moustaches,
and surveying the warriors with haughty
indulgence, would say—

"Fine animals. Brought any ivory? Yes? It's not
35 any too soon. Look at the muscles of that fellow—
third from the end. I wouldn't care to get a punch
on the nose from him. Fine arms, but legs no good
below the knee. Couldn't make cavalry men of
them." And after glancing down complacently at
his own shanks, he always concluded: "Pah! Don't 40
they stink! You, Makola! Take that herd over to
the storehouse and give them up some of the
rubbish you keep there. I'd rather see it full of
ivory than full of rags."

Kayerts approved. 45

Such profitable visits were rare. For days the two
pioneers of trade and progress would look on their
empty courtyard in the vibrating brilliance of
vertical sunshine. Below the high bank, the silent
river flowed on glittering and steady. On the sands 50
in the middle of the stream, hippos and alligators
sunned themselves side by side. And stretching
away in all directions, surrounding the
insignificant cleared spot of the trading post,
immense forests, hiding fateful complications of 55
fantastic life, lay in the eloquent silence of mute
greatness. The two men understood nothing,
cared for nothing but for the passage of days that
separated them from the steamer's return.

Their predecessor had left some torn books. They 60
also found some old copies of a home newspaper.
That print discussed what it was pleased to call
"Our Colonial Expansion" in high-flown
language. It spoke much of the rights and duties of
civilisation, of the sacredness of the civilising 65
work, and extolled the merits of those who went
about bringing light, and faith and commerce to
the dark places of the earth. Carlier and Kayerts
read, wondered, and began to think better of
themselves. Carlier said one evening, waving his 70
hand about, "In a hundred years, there will
perhaps be a town here. Quays, and warehouses, and
barracks, and—and—billiard-rooms. Civilisation,
my boy, and virtue—and all. And then, chaps will
read that two good fellows, Kayerts and Carlier, 75
were the first civilised men to live in this very
spot!" Kayerts nodded, "Yes, it is a consolation to
think of that."

(Joseph Conrad)

QUESTIONS FOR PART 1—INTERPRETATION

Questions on Passage 1

Marks

(a)   (i)   By referring to a word or phrase in paragraph 1 (lines 1–13), explain what is suggested about Robert Maxwell's lifestyle.   2

    (ii)   What is John Pilger's view about the reporting of Robert Maxwell's death and the reporting of the deaths in the Philippines?   1

    (iii)   By referring to paragraph 2 (lines 14–20), show how Pilger conveys his view.   2

(b)   "In one sense, the two events were connected." (line 21)

By referring to lines 22–41, explain the writer's view that there is a link between Maxwell and the deaths of the 6,000 Filipinos.   2

(c)   What "subtext" (underlying message) is referred to in line 47? You should refer to the next sentence. ("A typhoon, an earthquake . . . and charity.") in your answer.   2

(d)   (i)   Show how the information in parenthesis (lines 59–60) contributes to Pilger's argument at this stage.   2

    (ii)   In your own words, explain fully how, according to Pilger, television presented a "false neutrality" (line 69) in its coverage of the Ethiopian famine.   3

    (iii)   Comment on the tone of "the West's beloved stereotype of Third World dependence" (lines 73–75).   2

(e)   "This was illustrated when . . . wrote, 'Hell'." (lines 76–78)

Show how this sentence acts as a link between the two paragraphs.   2

(f)   "The majority of humanity . . . flit across the television screen." (lines 80–82)

Show how Pilger's word choice in this sentence conveys his view about the Western media's representation of the Third World.   3

(g)   By referring to lines 88–95, show how Pilger creates a climax to the passage. (In your answer, you may wish to refer to sentence structure, word choice, rhythm, ideas . . .)   4

      (25)

Questions on Passage 2

(h)   By referring to lines 1–19 (". . . never resting eyes."), show how Joseph Conrad develops the simile, "Kayerts and Carlier lived like blind men in a large room" (lines 1-2).   3

(i)   Show how the words spoken in lines 27–44 reveal each man's racism.   2

(j)   By commenting on particular words or phrases in lines 46–59, show how the author contrasts the trading post with its surrounding landscape.   2

(k)   (i)   Show how the context helps you to arrive at the meaning of "high-flown language". (lines 63–64)   2

    (ii)   Explain the irony of Carlier's words "In a hundred years . . . in this very spot!" (lines 71–77)   2

      (11)

Question on Both Passages

(l)   Joseph Conrad's short story about two Europeans living in Africa was written and is set in the 1890s; John Pilger is writing about the Third World and the West some 100 years later.

To what extent do these passages show that Western attitudes towards the Third World and its people have altered in this time? You should refer closely to both passages in your answer.   4

      (4)

Total (40)

PART 2—REPORT

READ THE INSTRUCTIONS BEFORE YOU ATTEMPT THIS QUESTION

(i) *The Millennium Commission—some information*

The Millennium Commission was set up by the government in 1994 to prepare plans for national celebrations of the millennium. It will receive 20% of the proceeds of the National Lottery until 31 December 2000. It is funded entirely through the proceeds of the Lottery. Camelot plc, the Lottery organiser, estimates that the Commission's income by the end of the year 2000 may reach £1·6 billion.

The Commission offers grants to three types of project:

Capital projects—around a dozen major "landmark" projects: "umbrella" applications, which group together smaller schemes with a common theme. Around £800 m will be available.

Millennium Awards—grants to hundreds of groups and individuals; £20 m available each year until 2000.

Millennium Exhibition and Festival
An Exhibition on the theme of Time will be sited on the Greenwich Peninsula in South East London (up to £200 m available); there is also to be a programme which will culminate in each part of the UK "owning" a week of the Exhibition.

Capital projects (in Scotland) include:

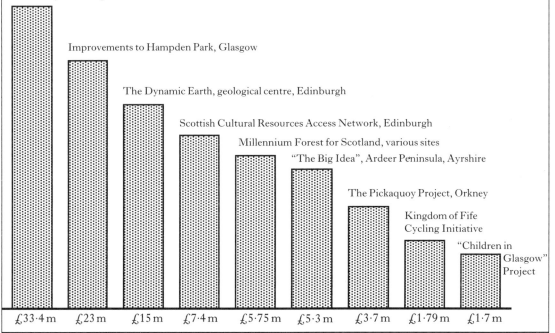

| £33·4 m | £23 m | £15 m | £7·4 m | £5·75 m | £5·3 m | £3·7 m | £1·79 m | £1·7 m |

Michael O'Connor, Director of Policy and Corporate Affairs at the Millennium Commission, explains: "The Commissions's funding strategy encompasses large and small capital projects, national celebrations and empowering individuals to make a contribution to the community. Together, these grant programmes extend opportunities to celebrate the millennium to communities across the UK."

THE MILLENNIUM

The items on pages 6, 7 and 8 relate to the topic of the "Millennium". Read them carefully.

You should spend approximately one hour on this part of the paper, which is worth 35 marks.

Your task is to write a report on the topic of the Millennium by selecting relevant information and reorganising the material provided. You might find it helpful to consider the following:

(*a*) why the millennium may be significant and plans already made to celebrate it;

(*b*) problems or controversies surrounding the millennium;

(*c*) benefits which may result from the celebration of the millennium.

You must base your report entirely on the material presented to you, and on any direct inferences you can draw from it. You should use your own words as far as possible. You should take an objective point of view. Write your report in formal, continuous prose. You are likely to be able to complete this task in about 400 words, but there is no penalty for exceeding the length.

(ii)   *A personal view—Robert Tremayne*

"Who will buy this wonderful morning . . .?"

There are at least three main issues in relation to the Millennium which concern me greatly.

To begin with, the date is quite arbitrary. The birth of Christ has been estimated by a variety of authorities as having taken place at any time up to 4 BC (as we call these years in present form). We may therefore have already passed the "true" millennium.

Secondly, the entire Chinese and Muslim worlds, up to three quarters of the population of the world, employ a different numbering system. The Muslim calendar has the year 2000 as its year 1421, and our year 2000 is, for the Chinese, simply the Year of the Dragon.

Further, the importance of the millennium as a significant point in world history (if indeed it is) has been hi-jacked by commercial concerns which want to get a jump ahead of their rivals. Already one Japanese car manufacturer has—it seems—"bought the rights" to the first sunrise of the year 2000. This will take place on the Chatham Islands, in the Pacific Ocean, close to the International Date Line, and the inhabitants have auctioned off the opportunity to record the arrival of the first rays of the sun on 1st January in the year 2000. Other reports suggest that already the greater part of the world's finest champagne has been bought up and stored away for consumption (only by the very rich, of course) at the millennium, while hotels—particularly in Scotland, which seems to have the world rights to New Year (Hogmanay) celebrations—and cruise companies report massive increases in advance bookings for the start of the next millennium.

For these reasons, then, it seems to be quite foolish to get excited by the turning of billions of second, minute and hour hands on billions of the world's clocks as they signify our movement from one not-very-special day to another. Indeed, maybe we should just pay more attention to the here and now, to the impoverished, the destitute, the homeless, those for whom there is at present little or no future, before concerning ourselves with another excuse for another celebration which is at best in bad taste, and at worst is an insult to those who have no part to play in it.

(iii) *A definition*

> A millennium is a period of 1,000 years. Some Christian sects believe that Jesus will return to govern the Earth in person at the next millennium.

(iv) *Some problems relating to the Millennium*

Every computer has a built-in clock, which also automatically keeps a note of the date. Until recently, date information on computers was limited to two digits in order to save space. As a result, 1986 was recorded as 86, 1997 as 97, and so on. The problem arises when we enter the year 2000: it becomes 00—which simply means nothing, an emptiness, a void, and many systems cannot cope with such a concept. Worse still, for some companies, bills will go unpaid, because they appear never to fall due; old stock is not used because it appears to be younger than newer stock or it appears not to exist at all, and service and maintenance schedules are turned upside down.

The cost to businesses worldwide could be in the region of $600 billion.

To mark the passing of an hour, you begin counting at 00.00; then one minute later will be 00.01, and so on until you reach 00.59. The hour is complete one minute later at 01.00. In the same way, then, the **century** is only complete at the **end** of the year 100, when we begin the year 101. Try it yourself—count from year 0 A.D. (the birth of Christ) and one year is up at the moment we reach year 1 A.D. So , a century is up at the **end** of the year 100, at the beginning of the year 101. To be correct, then, celebrations for the millennium should take place at the **end** of the year 2000, in 2001, not at the end of 1999, as most people are planning to do.

(v) *A personal view—P. Robinson*

AN OPPORTUNITY FOR RENEWAL

Why shouldn't the year 2000 be significant? The mathematics do not really matter—whether the millennium ends at the beginning or at the end of the year 2000. That number—2000—has a resonance, a ring to it, that few other numbers possess. It has a significance which spreads worldwide, which other dates cannot match, and because of this its arrival will be celebrated all over the world by hundreds of millions of people. It is therefore a unifying force; it contributes to international feeling and provides a common focus, maybe even a common purpose, for all the people of the world.

While every January provides an opportunity for individuals to think of what they are doing and where they are going, to renew themselves, maybe even re-invent themselves, the first January of the year 2000, the first month, year and decade of the next millennium will provide a special opportunity for the world as a whole to assess where it is going. We will have a unique chance to wipe the slate clean and re-dedicate ourselves to the future. Only once in a thousand years is a generation lucky enough to be able to mark, so dramatically, the passing of the old and the arrival of the new. It is to be hoped, then, that some world leaders will emerge who will provide the inspiration, the vision, to lift our eyes from mere champagne celebrations and look forward to the new era with hope for the future for all.

[END OF QUESTION PAPER]

SCOTTISH
CERTIFICATE OF
EDUCATION
1998

TUESDAY, 5 MAY
1.00 PM – 2.35 PM

ENGLISH
HIGHER GRADE
Paper II

There are **two parts** to this paper and you should attempt both parts.

In Part 1, you should attempt **either** Section A (Practical Criticism) **or** Section B (Close Reading of Specified Texts).

In Section A there are two optional questions for Practical Criticism. If you choose Section A, attempt only one of the two Practical Criticism questions.

In Section B there are nine optional questions on Specified Texts. If you choose Section B, attempt only one of the nine Specified Texts questions.

Each option in Part 1 is worth 25 marks.

In Part 2 (Critical Essay), you should attempt **one** question only, taken from any of the Sections A–D.

Your answer to Part 2 should begin on a fresh page.

Each question in Part 2 is worth 30 marks.

> NB You must not use, in any part of this paper, the same text(s) as you have used in your Review of Personal Reading.
>
> You must also pay attention to the instruction at the top of each Section in Part 2 about the use of genres and specified texts.

Index of Specified Texts/Authors in Part 1 Section B

1 *Romeo and Juliet*
2 Robert Burns
3 *North and South*
4 *The Devil's Disciple*
5 *The Inheritors*
6 Iain Crichton Smith
7 *Bold Girls*
8 *Sunset Song*
9 Philip Larkin

PART 1

You should spend approximately 45 minutes on this part of the paper.

SECTION A—PRACTICAL CRITICISM

If you choose this Section, attempt <u>either</u> Option 1 below <u>or</u> Option 2, which begins on Page four.

Option 1

Enter the letter corresponding to each question in the left-hand margin of your answer book.

Read the poem carefully and answer the questions which follow .

FARMER'S DEATH

Ke-uk, ke-uk, ke-uk, ki-kwaik,
The broon hens keckle and bouk,
And syne wi' their yalla beaks
For the reid worms houk.

5   The muckle white pig at the tail
O' the midden slotters and slorps,
But the auld ferm hoose is lown
And wae as a corpse.

The hen's een glitter like gless
10   As the worms gang twirlin' in,
But there's never a move in by
And the windas are blin'.

Feathers turn fire i' the licht,
The pig's doup skinkles like siller,
15   But the auld ferm hoose is waugh
Wi' the daith intill her.

Hen's cries are a panash in Heaven,
And a pig has the warld at its feet;
But wae for the hoose whaur a buirdly man
20   Crines in a windin' sheet.

Hugh MacDiarmid

Marks

(a) Show how the poet uses sound in lines 1–2 and lines 5–6 to portray hens and the pig respectively. **4**

(b) What contrast is made between the farmyard and the farmhouse in lines 1–8? **2**

(c) What impression are you given of the hen by the imagery and word choice of lines 9–10?
You should explain fully how this impression is given. **4**

(d) In lines 13–14 and lines 17–18, you are given further descriptions of both the hen and the pig. By close reference to the language of these lines, state what development in the significance of these animals you can detect. **4**

(e) By referring to the description of the farmhouse throughout the poem, show how the poet creates a particular mood. You should refer to three poetic techniques such as word choice, structure, sound, repetition, imagery. **6**

(f) How does the verse form enhance the impact of the poem? You may wish to refer to such features as structure, sound, syntax . . . **2**

(g) Does the poet's use of humour seem to you to add to or detract from the emotion of the poem? You should refer closely to the text in your answer. **3**

(25)

SECTION A—PRACTICAL CRITICISM (continued)

Option 2

Enter the letter corresponding to each question in the left-hand margin of your answer book.

Read the poem carefully and answer the questions which follow .

A LITTLE MORE

Each minute of a further light
Draws me towards perspective Spring.
I fold the minutes back each night,
 I hear the gossiping

5 Of birds whose instinct carries time,
A watch tucked in the flourished breast.
It ticks the second they must climb
 Into a narrow nest.

So birds. But I am not thus powered.
10 Impulse has gone. My measured cells
Of brain and knowledge are too stored,
 And trust to birds and bells.

Yet longer light is fetching me
To hopes I have no reason for.
15 A further lease of light each day
 Suggests irrational more.

Elizabeth Jennings

		Marks
(*a*)	At what season of the year and at what time of day is the poem set?	2
(*b*)	What does the image used in line 3 suggest to you about the mood of the poem? Justify your answer.	2
(*c*)	Show how the language in stanza 2 creates an impression of the birds and of their behaviour.	4
(*d*) (i)	Comment on the effectiveness of "So birds." (line 9) in relation to the structure of the poem.	2
(ii)	By referring to the word choice used in the rest of stanza 3, show how human behaviour contrasts with that of the birds.	4
(*e*) (i)	Comment on the function and position of "Yet" (line 13) in the argument of the poem.	2
(ii)	Comment on how the language of the last stanza suggests the idea that the speaker is not fully in control of her thoughts or feelings.	4
(*f*)	How does the verse form contribute to the impact or mood of the poem?	
	You may wish to consider such features as structure, sound, syntax . . .	2
(*g*)	Explain fully the relationship of the title to stanza 1 and to stanza 4.	3
		(25)

SECTION B—CLOSE READING OF SPECIFIED TEXTS

If you have chosen to attempt this Section, you should select only ONE text and answer the questions which follow it.

You should enter the number and the name of the text chosen at the top of the page, and the letter corresponding to each question in the left-hand margin of your answer book.

You are reminded of the instruction on the front cover about the use of texts.

1. *ROMEO AND JULIET*

Read the extract carefully and answer the questions which follow. The number of marks attached to each question will give a clear indication of the length of answer required.

This speech is taken from Act I Scene 1 of the play.

PRINCE:	Rebellious subjects, enemies to peace,
	Profaners of this neighbour-stainèd steel—
	Will they not hear? What, ho—you men, you beasts,
	That quench the fire of your pernicious rage
5	With purple fountains issuing from your veins!
	On pain of torture, from those bloody hands
	Throw your mistempered weapons to the ground
	And hear the sentence of your movèd prince.
	Three civil brawls, bred of an airy word
10	By thee, old Capulet, and Montague,
	Have thrice disturbed the quiet of our streets
	And made Verona's ancient citizens
	Cast by their grave-beseeming ornaments
	To wield old partisans, in hands as old,
15	Cankered with peace, to part your cankered hate.
	If ever you disturb our streets again,
	Your lives shall pay the forfeit of the peace.
	For this time all the rest depart away.
	You, Capulet, shall go along with me;
20	And, Montague, come you this afternoon,
	To know our farther pleasure in this case,
	To old Free-town, our common judgement-place.
	Once more, on pain of death, all men depart.

Exeunt all but Montague, his wife, and Benvolio

Marks

(a) By referring to lines 1 and 2, show how the Prince attempts to capture the attention of the crowd. **2**

(b) Why does the Prince pause at the end of line 2? **1**

(c) (i) How does the imagery used in lines 3–8 contribute to the Prince's description of himself as "movèd"? (line 8) **3**

    (ii) Comment on the use of the word "mistempered" in line 7. **2**

(d) "Three civil brawls . . . cankered hate." (lines 9–15)

What is the Prince's opinion of the incident which has just taken place?

Justify your answer by close reference to the text. **3**

(e) (i) In the last part of the speech (lines 16–23), how do such features as structure, content, the actor's delivery show the absolute authority of the Prince? **4**

    (ii) There are two other interventions by the Prince in the play.

Briefly state the circumstances of each. **2**

(f) To what extent do you feel that the decisions and behaviour of the older generation determine the fate of the younger generation in the play? **8**

(25)

You are reminded of the instruction on the front cover about the use of texts.

2. ROBERT BURNS

Read carefully the extract from *Tam O'Shanter,* and answer the questions which follow. The number of marks attached to each question will give a clear indication of the length of answer required.

The extract begins at the third stanza.

O *Tam*! hadst thou but been sae wise,
As ta'en thy ain wife *Kate's* advice!
She tauld thee weel thou was a skellum,
A blethering, blustering, drunken blellum;
5   That frae November till October,
Ae market-day thou was nae sober;
That ilka melder, wi' the miller,
Thou sat as lang as thou had siller;
That every naig was ca'd a shoe on;
10   The smith and thee gat roaring fou on;
That at the L—d's house, even on Sunday,
Thou drank wi' Kirkton Jean till Monday.
She prophesied that late or soon,
Thou would be found deep drown'd in Doon;
15   Or catch'd wi' warlocks in the mirk,
By *Alloway's* auld haunted kirk.

Ah, gentle dames! it gars me greet,
To think how mony counsels sweet,
How mony lengthen'd sage advices,
20   The husband frae the wife despises!

But to our tale: Ae market-night,
Tam had got planted unco right;
Fast by an ingle, bleezing finely,
Wi' reaming swats, that drank divinely;
25   And at his elbow, Souter *Johnny*,
His ancient, trusty, drouthy crony;
Tam lo'ed him like a vera brither;
They had been fou for weeks thegither.
The night drave on wi' sangs and clatter;
30   And ay the ale was growing better:
The landlady and *Tam* grew gracious,
Wi' favours, secret, sweet, and precious:
The Souter tauld his queerest stories;
The landlord's laugh was ready chorus:
35   The storm without might rair and rustle,
Tam did na mind the storm a whistle.

Care, mad to see a man sae happy,
E'en drown'd himsel amang the nappy:
As bees flee hame wi' lades o' treasure,
40   The minutes wing'd their way wi' pleasure:
Kings may be blest, but *Tam* was glorious,
O'er a' the ills o' life victorious!

But pleasures are like poppies spread,
You seize the flower, its bloom is shed;
45 Or like the snow falls in the river,
A moment white—then melts for ever;
Or like the borealis race,
That flit ere you can point their place;
Or like the rainbow's lovely form
50 Evanishing amid the storm.—
Nae man can tether time or tide;
The hour approaches *Tam* maun ride;
That hour, o' night's black arch the key-stane,
That dreary hour he mounts his beast in;
55 And sic a night he taks the road in,
As ne'er poor sinner was abroad in.

		Marks
(*a*)	Give two important background details which have been established before this extract.	2
(*b*)	(i) Comment on the effectiveness of the language used in lines 3 and 4 in conveying Kate's feelings about Tam.	2
	(ii) Show how the sentence structure of lines 3–12 contributes to their effectiveness in conveying Kate's feelings.	2
(*c*)	Lines 21–36 are highly effective in creating a particular atmosphere. Show how any **two** features such as rhyme, rhythm, sound and pace contribute to this atmosphere.	4
(*d*)	Choose one image from lines 43–50 and show how effective it is in conveying the theme of these lines.	3
(*e*)	Throughout the poem the reader is often aware of the intrusive voice of the narrator. By referring to **two** examples from this extract, show how Burns achieves different effects by means of this device.	4
(*f*)	Women often feature in the poems of Burns, sometimes as inspiration, sometimes as objects of criticism, sometimes as the butt of his humour. Briefly comment on how he presents them in *Tam O'Shanter*, then, more fully, consider his treatment of them in another poem.	8
		(25)

You are reminded of the instruction on the front cover about the use of texts.

3. *NORTH AND SOUTH*

Read the extract carefully and answer the questions which follow. The number of marks attached to each question will give a clear indication of the length of answer required.

The extract is taken from the early part of the novel.

"I shall not be at home till evening. I am going to Bracy Common, and will ask Farmer Dobson to give me something for dinner. I shall be back to tea at seven."

5 He did not look at either of them, but Margaret knew what he meant. By seven the announcement must be made to her mother. Mr Hale would have delayed making it till half-past six, but Margaret was of different stuff. She could not bear the impending weight on her mind all the day long: better get the worst over; the day would be too short to comfort her mother. But while she stood by the window, thinking how to begin, and waiting for the servant to have left the room, her mother had gone up-stairs to put on her things to go to the school. She came down ready equipped, in a brisker mood than usual.

"Mother, come round the garden with me this morning; just one turn," said Margaret, putting her arm
10 round Mrs Hale's waist.

They passed through the open window. Mrs Hale spoke — said something — Margaret could not tell what. Her eye caught on a bee entering a deep-belled flower: when that bee flew forth with his spoil she would begin — that should be the sign. Out he came.

"Mamma! Papa is going to leave Helstone!" she blurted forth. "He's going to leave the Church, and
15 live in Milton-Northern." There were the three hard facts hardly spoken.

"What makes you say so?" asked Mrs Hale, in a surprised incredulous voice. "Who has been telling you such nonsense?"

"Papa himself," said Margaret, longing to say something gentle and consoling, but literally not knowing how. They were close to a garden-bench. Mrs Hale sat down and began to cry.

20 "I don't understand you," she said. "Either you have made some great mistake, or I don't quite understand you."

"No, mother, I have made no mistake. Papa has written to the bishop, saying that he has such doubts that he cannot conscientiously remain a priest of the Church of England, and that he must give up Helstone. He has also consulted Mr Bell—Frederick's godfather, you know, mamma; and it is arranged
25 that we go to live in Milton-Northern." Mrs Hale looked up in Margaret's face all the time she was speaking these words: the shadow on her countenance told that she, at least, believed in the truth of what she said.

"I don't think it can be true," said Mrs Hale, at length. "He would surely have told me before it came to this."

30 It came strongly upon Margaret's mind that her mother ought to have been told: that whatever her faults of discontent and repining might have been, it was an error in her father to have left her to learn his change of opinion, and his approaching change of life, from her better-informed child. Margaret sat down by her mother, and took her unresisting head on her breast, bending her own soft cheeks down caressingly to touch her face.

35 "Dear, darling, mamma! we were so afraid of giving you pain. Papa felt so acutely—you know you are not strong, and there must have been such terrible suspense to go through."

"When did he tell you, Margaret?"

"Yesterday, only yesterday," replied Margaret, detecting the jealousy which prompted the inquiry. "Poor papa!"—trying to divert her mother's thoughts into compassionate sympathy for all her father
40 had gone through. Mrs Hale raised her head.

"What does he mean by having doubts?" she asked. "Surely, he does not mean that he thinks differently—that he knows better than the Church."

Margaret shook her head, and the tears came into her eyes, as her mother touched the bare nerve of her own regret.

45 "Can't the bishop set him right?" asked Mrs Hale, half impatiently.

"I'm afraid not," said Margaret. "But I did not ask. I could not bear to hear what he might answer. It is all settled at any rate. He is going to leave Helstone in a fortnight. I am not sure if he did not say he had sent in his deed of resignation."

"In a fortnight!" exclaimed Mrs Hale, "I do think this is very strange — not at all right. I call it very
50 unfeeling," said she, beginning to take relief in tears. "He has doubts, you say, and gives up his living, and all without consulting me. I dare say, if he had told me his doubts at the first I could have nipped them in the bud."

Marks

(*a*) What major event had occurred in Margaret's life on the same day that her father confided in her about his decision to leave the church?   2

(*b*) (i) Mrs Hale's mood is described as "brisker" in line 8. Up until this point in the novel what has been Mrs Hale's more usual mood?   1

　　　 (ii) What seems to be the main reason for her feeling this way?   2

(*c*) How does the sentence structure of lines 11–13 reflect Margaret's thoughts and feelings at this moment?   4

(*d*) "'Mamma! Papa is going to leave Helstone . . . facts hardly spoken." (lines 14–15)

　　　 By referring closely to the language of these lines, show how the manner in which Margaret broke the news to her mother is conveyed.   2

(*e*) Examine Mrs Hale's words from "I don't think . . ." (line 28) to the end of the extract. Trace the development of her reaction to the news.   4

(*f*) Show how the image in lines 43–44 reveals Margaret's feelings about her father's behaviour.   2

(*g*) In the latter part of the novel Margaret returns to the South and she and Mr Thornton both experience a reversal of fortune.

　　　 Explain what happens to each and discuss to what extent you find their reconciliation to be convincing.   8

(25)

You are reminded of the instruction on the front cover about the use of texts.

4.   *THE DEVIL'S DISCIPLE*

Read the extract carefully and answer the questions which follow. The number of marks attached to each question will give a clear indication of the length of answer required.

Reverend Anderson returns from a visit to Richard Dudgeon's house.

JUDITH: [*almost in tears, as if the visit were a personal humiliation to her*] But why did you go there?

ANDERSON: [*gravely*] Well, it is all the talk that Major Swindon is going to do what he did in Springtown—make an example of some notorious rebel, as he calls us. He pounced
5   on Peter Dudgeon as the worst character there; and it is the general belief that he will pounce on Richard as the worst here.

JUDITH: But Richard said—

ANDERSON: [*goodhumoredly cutting her short*] Pooh! Richard said! He said what he thought would frighten you and frighten me, my dear. He said what perhaps (God forgive
10   him!) he would like to believe. It's a terrible thing to think of what death must mean for a man like that. I felt that I must warn him. I left a message for him.

JUDITH: [*querulously*] What message?

ANDERSON: Only that I should be glad to see him for a moment on a matter of importance to himself, and that if he would look in here when he was passing he would be welcome.

15   JUDITH: [*aghast*] You asked that man to come here!

ANDERSON: I did.

JUDITH: [*sinking on the seat and clasping her hands*] I hope he wont come! Oh, I pray that he may not come!

ANDERSON: Why? Dont you want him to be warned?

20   JUDITH: He must know his danger. Oh, Tony, is it wrong to hate a blasphemer and a villain? I do hate him. I cant get him out of my mind: I know he will bring harm with him. He insulted you: he insulted me: he insulted his mother.

ANDERSON: [*quaintly*] Well, dear, lets forgive him; and then it wont matter.

JUDITH: Oh, I know it's wrong to hate anybody; but—

25   ANDERSON: [*going over to her with humorous tenderness*] Come, dear, youre not so wicked as you think. The worst sin towards our fellow creatures is not to hate them, but to be indifferent to them; thats the essence of inhumanity. After all, my dear, if you watch people carefully, youll be surprised to find how like hate is to love. [*She starts, strangely touched—even appalled. He is amused at her.*] Yes: I'm quite in earnest.
30   Think of how some of our married friends worry one another, tax one another, are jealous of one another, cant bear to let one another out of sight for a day, are more like jailers and slave-owners than lovers. Think of those very same people with their enemies, scrupulous, lofty, self-respecting, determined to be independent of one another, careful of how they speak of one another—pooh! havnt you often thought
35   that if they only knew it, they were better friends to their enemies than to their own husbands and wives? Come: depend on it, my dear, you are really fonder of Richard than you are of me, if you only knew it. Eh?

JUDITH: Oh, dont say that: dont say that, Tony, even in jest. You dont know what a horrible feeling it gives me.

40   ANDERSON: [*laughing*] Well, well: never mind, pet. He's a bad man; and you hate him as he deserves. And youre going to make the tea, arnt you?

Marks

(a) Explain why Judith is "*almost in tears*" (line 1).   2

(b) By referring to lines 8–11, explain what is revealed about Anderson's attitude to Richard.   2

(c) By examining the language of Judith's speeches (lines 15 to 24), show how she attempts to persuade Anderson to her way of thinking.   4

(d) Identify and explain **two** examples of Shaw's use of dramatic irony in Anderson's speech (lines 25–37).   4

(e) (i) What, in your opinion, is the tone of Anderson's speech (lines 40–41)? Support your opinion by textual reference.   2

     (ii) By referring to elsewhere in the extract, show whether this tone towards his wife is consistent.   3

(f) "... they were better friends to their enemies ..." (line 35)

The play features a number of improbable alliances and unlikely friendships. Discuss **two** relationships which contribute to your appreciation of the play.   8

(25)

You are reminded of the instruction on the front cover about the use of texts.

5.   *THE INHERITORS*

Read the extract carefully and answer the questions which follow. The number of marks attached to each question will give a clear indication of the length of answer required.

In this extract the old woman is trying to get "the people" to come to terms with recent events in their lives.

The old woman turned from the fire and spoke to them:

"Now there is Lok."

He looked at her blankly. Fa bent her head. The old woman came to him, took him firmly by the hand and led him to one side. Here was the Mal place. She made Lok sit down, his back against the rock, his
5   hams in the smooth earthen dip that Mal had worn. The strangeness of this overcame Lok. He looked sideways at the water, then back at the people and laughed. There were eyes everywhere, and they waited for him. He was at the head of the procession not at the back of it, and every picture went right out of his head. The blood made his face hot and he pressed his hands over his eyes. He looked through his fingers at the women, at Liku, then down at the mound where the body of Mal was buried. He
10   wished urgently to talk to Mal, to wait quietly before him to be told what to do. But no voice came from the mound and no picture. He grasped at the first picture that came into his head.

"I dreamed. The other was chasing me. Then we were together."

Nil lifted the new one to her breast.

"I dreamed. Ha lay with me and with Fa. Lok lay with Fa and with me."

15   She began to whimper. The old woman made a gesture that startled and silenced her.

"A man for pictures. A woman for Oa. Ha and Mal have gone. Now there is Lok."

Lok's voice came out small, like Liku's.

"To-day we shall hunt for food."

The old woman waited pitilessly. There was still food piled in the recess, though little enough was left.
20   What people would hunt for food when they were not hungry and there was food left to eat? Fa squatted forward. While she was speaking some of the confusion died away in Lok's head. He did not listen to Fa.

"I have a picture. The other is hunting for food and the people are hunting . . ."

She looked the old woman daringly in the eye.

25   "Then the people are hungry."

Nil rubbed her back against the rock.

"That is a bad picture."

The old woman shouted over them.

"Now there is Lok!"

30   Lok remembered. He took his hands from his face.

"I have seen the other. He is on the island. He jumps from rock to rock. He climbs in the trees. He is dark. He changes shape like a bear in a cave."

The people looked outward to the island. It was full of sunlight and a mist of green leaves. Lok called them back.

35   "And I followed his scent. He was there ". . . and he pointed to the roof of the overhang so that they all looked up . . ." he stayed and watched us. He is like a cat and he is not like a cat. He is also like, like . . ."

The pictures went out of his head for a while. He scratched himself under the mouth. There were so many things to be said. He wished he could ask Mal what it was that joined a picture to a picture so that
40   the last of many came out of the first.

"Perhaps Ha is not in the river. Perhaps he is on the island with the other. Ha was a mighty jumper."

The people looked along the terrace to the place where the detached rocks of the island swept in towards the bank. Nil pulled the new one from her breast and let him crawl on the earth. The water fell from her eyes.

45   "That is a good picture."

"I will speak with the other. How can he always be on the island? I will hunt for a new scent." Fa was tapping her palm against her mouth.

"Perhaps he came out of the island. Like out of a woman. Or out of the fall."

"I do not see this picture."

50   Now Lok found how easy it was to speak the words to others who would heed them. There need not even be a picture with the words.

"Fa will look for a scent and Nil and Liku and the new one . . . ."

The old woman would not interrupt him. She seized a great bough instead and hurled it into the fire. Lok sprang to his feet with a cry, and then was silent. The old woman spoke for him.

55   "Lok will not want Liku to go. There is no man. Let Fa and Lok go. This is what Lok says."

He looked at her in bewilderment and her eyes told him nothing. He began to shake his head.

"Yes," he said, "Yes."

Marks

(a)   "Now there is Lok." (line 2)

Explain the significance of the old woman's statement and what has brought this situation about.   3

(b)   By close reference to lines 3–11, show how the writer suggests that Lok may not be suitable for his new role.   4

(c)   "A man for pictures. A woman for Oa." (line 16)

Explain how Lok's people use "pictures". Comment on **two** examples from this extract.   4

(d)   (i)   By referring to **one** example of the old woman's words in this extract, explain her significance in the lives of "the people".   2

   (ii)   By referring to other parts of the novel, explain how her significance is confirmed.   4

(e)   "She looked the old woman daringly in the eye." (line 24)

By referring to incidents which happen after this extract, show how Fa's behaviour here is an important signal in the development of her relationship with Lok.   8

(25)

120

You are reminded of the instruction on the front cover about the use of texts.

6. IAIN CRICHTON SMITH

Read the poem carefully and answer the questions which follow. The number of marks attached to each question will give a clear indication of the length of answer required.

At the Highland Games

Like re-reading a book which has lost its pith.

Watching the piper dandying over a sodden stage
saluting an empty tent.

The empty beer glasses catch the sun
5   sparkle like old brooches against green.

Fur-hatted, with his huge twirling silver stick
the pipe-major has gypsy cheekbones, colour of brick.

Everything drowses. The stewards with aloof eagle stare
sit on collapsing rock, chair on brown chair.

10   Once the pibroch showed the grave 'ground'
of seas without bubbles, where great hulks were drowned,

meat with moustaches. The heroic dead die
over and over the sea to misty Skye.

Past the phantom ivy, bird song, I walk
15   among crew-cuts, cameras, the heather-covered rock,

past my ancestry, peasants, men who bowed
with stony necks to the daughter-stealing lord.

Past my ancestry, the old songs, the pibroch
stirring my consciousness like the breeze a loch.

20   Past my buried heart my friend who complains
of "All the crime, their insane violence."

Stone by stone the castles crumble. The seas
have stored away their great elegies.

"Morag of Dunvegan." Dandy piper
25   with delicate soft paws, knee-bending stepper,

saluting an empty tent. Blue-kilted stewards
strut like strange storks along the sodden sward.

Finished. All of it's finished. The Gaelic
boils in my mouth, the South Sea silver stick

30   twirls, settles. The mannequins are here.
Calum, how you'd talk of their glassy stare,

their loud public voices. Stained pictures
of what was raw, violent, alive and coarse.

I watch their heirs, Caligulas with canes
35   stalk in their rainbow kilts towards the dance.

Marks

(*a*)　(i)　How does the first line reveal the attitude of the poet to the Highland Games?　　2

　　　(ii)　Show, by close references to lines 2–9, how this attitude develops.　　3

(*b*)　Briefly explain one way in which lines 10–13 contrast with lines 1–9.　　2

(*c*)　Show how **two** of the following are effective in conveying the poet's further reflections in lines 14–21:

　　(i)　repetition;　　　　(iv)　sentence structure;

　　(ii)　word choice;　　　(v)　sound.

　　(iii)　imagery;　　4

(*d*)　(i)　What does the second reference to either the piper (line 24) or to the stewards (line 26) contribute to your understanding of the ideas of the poem?　　2

　　　(ii)　By referring to any **two** of the following, show how they contribute to the tone of the conclusion:

　　　　　mannequins (line 30);

　　　　　Stained pictures (line 32);

　　　　　Caligulas with canes (line 34).　　4

(*e*)　By close reference to any other poem by Iain Crichton Smith, show how he examines aspects of the past in order to support a view he has of the present.　　8

(25)

You are reminded of the instruction on the front cover about the use of texts.

7. *BOLD GIRLS*

Read the extract carefully and answer the questions which follow. The number of marks attached to each question will give a clear indication of the length of answer required.

The extract is from Scene 2 in the club. Cassie has got up to dance alone.

NORA: Holy Mother of God, what is she doing?

MARIE: I don't know, Nora.

NORA: Oh Marie get up with her!

MARIE: What!

5   NORA: We can't leave her on her own there, performing for the whole town!

Cassie's dancing becomes more extravagant.

NORA: Marie!

MARIE (*getting up*): Oh Nora I don't even like dancing.

Marie crosses over and joins Cassie who beams, applauding her. Marie starts shuffling cautiously from foot

10 *to foot.*

CASSIE: I'm telling you this is a great diet Marie, you really feel the benefit of the gin.

MARIE: Well maybe you should go easy now, Cassie.

CASSIE: Oh I'm a long way from lockjawed.

Nora is beckoning at them frantically.

15 MARIE: Your mummy's asking us to come and sit down.

CASSIE: The song's just started.

Marie glances round nervously.

What? Are they all watching us?

MARIE: They are.

20 CASSIE: Let them.

MARIE (*with a shaky laugh*): Feel a bit like the last meat pie in the shop out here, Cassie.

CASSIE: Well let them stay hungry. They can just look and think what they like.

MARIE: Cassie, what's wrong?

CASSIE: Oh, I'm just bad Marie, didn't you know?

25 MARIE: No. I never knew that.

CASSIE: You remember that wee girl in Turf Lodge, the one Martin couldn't get enough of? She was a decent wee girl. She's bad now. Ask my mummy.

MARIE: Have you had words?

CASSIE: He's out in less than a year, Marie.

30 MARIE: *Martin*!?

CASSIE: Joe.

MARIE: I know. It'll be all right Cassie.

They stop dancing, they look at each other.

It'll be alright, Cassie.

35 CASSIE: I tell you Marie I can't stand the *smell* of him. The greasy, grinning, beer bellied smell of him. And he's winking away about all he's been dreaming of, wriggling his fat fingers over me like I'm a poke of chips—I don't want him in the house in my *bed*, Marie.

MARIE: You'll cope.

CASSIE: Oh I'm just bad. I am.

40 MARIE: Don't. Don't say that about yourself.

CASSIE: I'll go crazy.

MARIE: I won't let you. You won't get a chance Cassie, I'll just be across the road, I won't let you go crazy. You just see what you'll get if you try it.

Slowly Cassie smiles at her.

45   (*Putting a hand on Cassie's arm*) Now will you come and sit down?

The doors at the back bang open.

Hard white light floods everything.

Oh Jesus it's a raid!

All the women freeze, legs apart, arms raised as if they're being searched.

50   *The same hard light stays on them.*

DEIRDRE: Brick in your hand, hard in your hand, hit skin and it'll burst open and bleed, hit bones and they'll break, you can hear them break, hear them snap.

MARIE: Why are you asking my name, you know my name.

DEIRDRE: Smell the petrol, lungs full of the smell of it. Blow it out again and you'll be breathing
55   fire. Throw fire in a bottle and it runs everywhere like it's water.

MARIE: Everyone knows where I live.

DEIRDRE: Get a car, fast car, drive it till its wheels burn, leave it smoking, burning, exploding.

MARIE: Everyone knows all about me, don't they? So what do you want to know? What do you want?

60   DEIRDRE: The whole town's a prison, smash chunks off the walls 'cause we're all in a prison.

Cut the hard white light.

		Marks
(*a*)	What is the basis of Cassie's "great diet" (line 11)?	1
(*b*)	Show how in lines 2–22 the playwright contrasts the characters of Marie and Cassie through their language and actions.	4
(*c*)	By close reference to two language features in lines 35–37, show how Cassie reveals her attitude towards Joe.	4
(*d*)	Look at the section from line 49 to the end of the extract.	
	(i) In this section of the extract the dramatic style of the play has changed. What features contribute to this change of style?	4
	(ii) What do Deirdre's speeches in this section suggest about her personality? (You should refer closely to lines 51–60.)	4
(*e*)	How effective do you find the sudden changes of style in *Bold Girls*? Refer briefly to this extract, and to other relevant occasions in the play.	
	You may wish to refer to how they affect revelation of character, exploration of theme, dramatic impact . . .	8
		(25)

You are reminded of the instruction on the front cover about the use of texts.

8. *SUNSET SONG*

Read the extract carefully and answer the questions which follow. The number of marks attached to each question will give a clear indication of the length of answer required.

The extract is taken from "Harvest".

But Chris didn't care, sitting there at Blawearie with young Ewan at her breast, her man beside her, Blawearie theirs and the grain a fine price, forbye that the stirks sold well in the marts. Maybe there was war and bloodshed and that was awful, but far off also, you'd hear it like the North Sea cry in a morning, a crying and a thunder that became unending as the weeks went by, part of life's plan, fringing
5 the horizon of your days with its pelt and uproar. So the new year came in and Chris watched young Ewan change and grow there at her breast, he was quick of temper like his father, good like his mother, she told Ewan; and Ewan laughed *God, maybe you're right! You could hardly be wrong in a thing after bringing a bairn like that in the world.* And she laughed at him *But you helped a little!* and he blushed as red as he always did, they seemed daft as ever in their love as the days wore on. It was still as strange
10 and as kind to lie with him, live with him, watch the sweat on his forehead when he came from tramping a day in the parks at the heels of his horses; still miracle to hear beside her his soundless breathing in the dark of the night when their pleasure was past and he slept so soon. But she didn't herself, those nights as the Winter wore to March, into Spring: she'd lie and listen to that hushed breathing of his one side of her, the boy's quicker breath in his cradle out by—content, content, what more could she have or
15 want than the two of them, body and blood and breath? And morning would bring her out of her bed to tend young Ewan and make the breakfast and clean out the byre and the stable, singing; she worked never knowing she tired and Long Rob of the Mill came on her one morning as she cleaned the manure from the stable and he cried *The Spring of life, eh, Chris quean? Sing it and cherish it, 'twill never come again!*

20 Different from the old Rob he looked, she thought, but thought that carelessly, hurried to be in to young Ewan. But she stopped and watched him swing down the rigs to Ewan by the side of his horses, Ewan with his horses halted on the side of the brae and the breath of them rising up like a steam. And she heard Ewan call *Ay, man, Rob,* and Rob call *Ay, man, Ewan,* and they called the truth, they seemed fine men both against the horizon of Spring, their feet deep laired in the wet clay ground, brown and
25 great, with their feet on the earth and the sky that waited behind. And Chris looked at them over-long, they glimmered to her eyes as though they had ceased to be there, mirages of men dreamt by a land grown desolate against its changing sky. And the Chris that had ruled those other two selves of herself, content, unquestioning these many months now, shook her head and called herself daft.

Marks

(a) Comment on the effectiveness of the extended simile, "like the North Sea . . . pelt and uproar" (lines 3–5), to describe Chris's view of the war.   3

(b) (i) What is revealed about the relationship between Chris and Ewan by lines 7–9 ("and Ewan laughed . . . as the days wore on.")?   2

   (ii) By referring to the language of lines 9–17 ("It was still as strange . . . knowing she tired"), show how a convincing picture of Chris's contentment is conveyed.   4

(c) Show how Long Rob's words (lines 18–19) act as a link between the two paragraphs.   2

(d) By commenting on particular words and phrases, show how Chris's mood develops (lines 20–28).   6

(e) To what extent do you find the ending of *Sunset Song* to be pessimistic? In your answer you should refer briefly to the passage and more fully to the remainder of "Harvest" and to the last section of the novel, "The Unfurrowed Field".   8

(25)

You are reminded of the instruction on the front cover about the use of texts.

9. PHILIP LARKIN

Read the poem carefully and answer the questions which follow. The number of marks attached to each question will give a clear indication of the length of answer required.

REASONS FOR ATTENDANCE

The trumpet's voice, loud and authoritative,
Draws me a moment to the lighted glass
To watch the dancers—all under twenty-five—
Shifting intently, face to flushed face,
5 Solemnly on the beat of happiness.

—Or so I fancy, sensing the smoke and sweat,
The wonderful feel of girls. Why be out here?
But then, why be in there? Sex, yes, but what
Is sex? Surely, to think the lion's share
10 Of happiness is found by couples—sheer

Inaccuracy, as far as I'm concerned.
What calls me is that lifted, rough-tongued bell
(Art, if you like) whose individual sound
Insists I too am individual.
15 It speaks; I hear; others may hear as well,

But not for me, nor I for them; and so
With happiness. Therefore I stay outside,
Believing this; and they maul to and fro,
Believing that; and both are satisfied,
20 If no one has misjudged himself. Or lied.

30 December 1953

		Marks
(a)	Choose one example of word choice in lines 3–5 and show how it conveys the poet's attitude to "the dancers".	2
(b)	(i) "—Or so I fancy . . ." (line 6) In what way does this opening to verse two signal a change in the poet's attitude?	1
	(ii) Show how sentence structure in lines 6–9 reflects his state of mind.	4
(c)	"—sheer Inaccuracy, as far as I'm concerned." (lines 10–11) Comment on the effectiveness of one poetic technique in these lines in developing the ideas of the poem.	2
(d)	By commenting on references to music in the poem, show how the poet illustrates the difference between himself and the dancers.	4
(e)	"If no one has misjudged himself. Or lied." (line 20) Explain the meaning of the last line and comment on its effectiveness as a conclusion to the poem.	4
(f)	It has been said that the titles of Larkin's poems are often extremely significant. After briefly giving your views on the contribution of the title to the meaning of this poem, discuss more fully how the title of another of his poems is important to your understanding of that poem.	8
		(25)

PART 2—CRITICAL ESSAY

Attempt ONE question only, taken from any of the Sections A to D.

In all Sections you may use Scottish texts.

You should spend about 50 minutes on this part of the paper.

Begin your answer on a fresh page.

If you use a Specified Text as the basis for your Critical Essay, you must not rely ONLY on any extract printed in Part 1 in this paper. If you attempt Section C—Poetry, you should note the additional instruction at the head of Section C.

SECTION A—DRAMA

> **If you have answered on a play in the Specified Text option in Part 1 of the paper, you must not attempt a question from this Drama Section.**
>
> **In your answer in this Section you should, where relevant, refer to such features as dialogue, characterisation, plot, theme, scene, climax, style, structure . . .**

1. By referring closely to one or more than one episode in a Shakespearean play, show how you were made to feel a range of emotions.

2. Many dramatists make use of very restricted settings—for example, a workplace, a house, or even a single room—for most of the play.

   Choose a play whose setting is restricted in this way and examine the use the dramatist makes of the setting to develop features such as character, theme, mood . . .

3. Consider a play in the course of which one of the major characters changes significantly. Outline the nature of the change, and go on to discuss to what extent the dramatist convinces you that the change is credible and consistent with the play's theme.

4. (*a*) Choose a play which you have studied and examine the features it has which would make its performance have an impact on a theatre audience.

   (You might wish to refer to such things as visual impact; effective use of sound; tension; humour; moments of high emotion . . .)

   OR

   (*b*) Name a play you have read and seen in performance and examine the features of the text and the performance which made an impact on you.

   (You might wish to refer to such things as visual impact; effective use of sound; tension; humour; moments of high emotion . . .)

5. Choose a play which you found genuinely funny in places, yet which had also a serious theme. By referring closely to the text, explain the humour and the seriousness that underlies it.

SECTION B—PROSE

If you have answered on a prose work in the Specified Text option in Part 1 of the paper, you must not attempt a question from this Prose Section.

In your answer in this Section you should, where relevant, refer to such features as setting, theme, characterisation, plot, content, style, structure, language, narrative stance, symbolism . . .

---

6. Sometimes the significance of the title of a novel or short story is not immediately obvious.

   Choose a novel or short story which fits this description, and show how, after careful study, the full significance of the title becomes clear.

7. "Non-fiction is seldom objective. Often it sways your feelings or influences your thoughts."

   By referring closely to a work of non-fiction (such as an essay, a piece of journalism, a biography, a travel book . . .), show how the writer does more than simply convey information.

8. Choose a novel or short story whose structure is based on a journey or a quest. Show how the writer makes use of this structure to develop character and theme.

   (The journey or quest could be literal or metaphorical.)

9. What was your reaction to the ending of a novel you have read? By referring closely to the ending and to its relationship with the whole text, explain why you felt as you did.

SECTION C—POETRY

If you have answered on a poem in the Specified Text option in Part 1 of the paper, you must not attempt a question from this Poetry Section. You may not base an answer on Burns's "Tam O' Shanter", Crichton Smith's "At the Highland Games" or Larkin's "Reasons for Attendance".

In your answer in this Section you should, where relevant, refer to such features as rhyme, rhythm, word choice, language, sound, imagery, symbolism, style, structure . . .

---

10. Many poems are concerned with a sense of loss or deep sadness at a particular event.

    Examine the means by which a poet, in one poem, conveys either of these emotions to you.

11. Is there a poem which has genuinely shocked or inspired you?

    Explain what aspects of the poem's language and ideas produced this response.

12. Choose a poem which appeals to you because certain words, or lines, or even the whole poem, can be interpreted in more than one way.

    By referring closely to the text, discuss these ambiguities and show to what extent they contribute to your appreciation of the poem as a whole.

13. Sometimes a reader can admire the techniques of a particular poem yet disagree or lack sympathy with some of the ideas it conveys.

    Select a poem which fits this description and, by close reference to the text, justify your view of the techniques and the ideas.

SECTION D—MASS MEDIA

If your Review of Personal Reading is based entirely on a radio, television or film script, you must not attempt a question from this Mass Media Section.

14. By referring closely to one film, select and analyse a sequence which you feel is technically effective, explaining how it contributes to your understanding of the film's deeper theme(s). (You may wish to refer in your answer to mise-en-scène, montage and soundtrack.)

15. By referring closely to a film you have studied, show to what extent its artistic merit has been affected by commercial considerations.

16. Sometimes our personal views of an individual are influenced by the representations constructed by the media. By referring closely to artefacts from more than one medium, show how these representations have influenced your views of one such individual.

17. "We're trapped—somewhere between Brigadoon and Braveheart."
 Are you satisfied with representations of Scotland and the Scots in one particular medium? (You should refer closely to your chosen text(s) in your answer.)

18. By referring closely to one, or more than one television drama you have studied, show how a particular ideology shaped aspects of the text(s).

19. To what extent does the success of a television drama (such as a soap opera, a series, a serial . . .) depend on its representations of contrasting groups—young and old, rich and poor, locals and outsiders . . .?

[END OF QUESTION PAPER]

NOTES

NOTES

ACKNOWLEDGEMENT

Waiting Room
by
Moira Andrew

First published in *New Poetry 8*, An Arts Council Anthology
edited by John Fuller, (Hutchinson & Co, 1982)

Printed by Bell & Bain Ltd., Glasgow, Scotland.